Public Speaking
A Competency-Based Approach

William Huddy, Ph.D.
Michael Monsour, Ph.D.

Metropolitan State University, Denver

FOUNTAINHEAD
PRESS

As a textbook publisher, we are faced with enormous environmental issues due the large amount of paper contained in our print products. Since our inception in 2002, we have worked diligently to be as eco-friendly as possible.

Our "green" initiatives include:

Electronic Products
We deliver products in non-paper form whenever possible. This includes pdf downloadables, flash drives, & CD's.

Electronic Samples
We use a new electronic sampling system, called Xample. Instructor samples are sent via a personalized web page that links to pdf downloads.

FSC Certified Printers
All of our Printers are certified by the Forest Service Council which promotes environmentally and socially responsible management of the world's forests. This program allows consumer groups, individual consumers and businesses to work together hand in hand to promote responsible use of the world's forests as a renewable and sustainable resource.

Recycled Paper
Almost all of our products are printed on a minimum of 10-30% post consumer waste recycled paper.

Support of Green Causes
When we do print, we donate a portion of our revenue to Green causes. Listed below are a few of the organizations that have received donations from Fountainhead Press. We welcome your feedback and suggestions for contributions, as we are always searching for worthy initiatives.
Rainforest 2 Reef
Environmental Working Group

For information, please call or write:
1-800-586-0330
Fountainhead Press
Southlake, TX 76092

Web site: www.fountainheadpress.com
E-mail: customerservice@fountainheadpress.com

ISBN: 978-1-68036-112-4

Printed in the United States of America

Table of Contents

Introduction and Acknowledgements

Welcome to SPE 1010 Public Speaking! My name is Mike Monsour, and I'm the SPE Coordinator for the Department of Communication Arts and Sciences (CAS). We teach between 70 and 80 sections of public speaking during the fall and spring semesters, and an additional 15 sections in the summer. You are one of thousands who take this course every year. CAS has two primary pedagogical goals in teaching this class: 1) to provide you with the skills to become a competent public speaker; and 2) to help you become a much better listener and critic of the speeches you hear from others in our society, from politicians—to preachers—to lobbyists.

Professor William Huddy and I constructed this workbook to streamline your public speaking experience and to add a degree of consistency from one section to another. As you will see from the Table of Contents, this workbook includes, among other things, 1) copies of *evaluation forms* that you will be using to critique your classmates on their required five speeches; 2) a sample of how to do the *preparation outline* that is required with all of your speeches; 3) the *attendance* policy; 4) the *grievance* policy; 5) a description of *Monroe's Motivated Sequence*; 6) a description of the Speech Communication Major and what you can do with a Speech Communication Degree; 7) a description of the *"Spectacular Vernacular,"* the public speaking contest we have every April with cash prizes; and finally, 8) a description of each of the five speeches you will give this semester!

The Department of Communication Arts and Sciences uses a *competency-based approach* to this course. The decision to move to a competency-based approach to teaching public speaking was largely based on literature suggesting that such an approach leads to measurable and increased public speaking competencies. A competency based approach helps to ensure that once you complete SPE 1010 Public Speaking you will have the eight competencies necessary to publicly present in a variety of contexts from one-on-one sales pitches to a more structured public speech in your community or at work. Perhaps sadly, all of us at one time or another will have an opportunity, and it is an opportunity, to eulogize a deceased family member or friend. And on the flip side, you'll want to experience the elation of leading a toast to your best friend at their wedding or retirement, or simply recognition of a job well done! This class will give you the confidence and courage to convey your thoughts of friendship and encouragement in large group settings.

After completing this course you'll be able to give a speech that is organized, clear, maximally informative, and persuasive (when the situation calls for persuasion). You'll also develop important nonverbal skills such as how to have effective and natural gestures, how to use eye contact to establish bonding with your audience, and how to use the physical space given to you in a public speaking situation. Equally important, you'll learn how to use language to verbally express yourself in a way that's interesting and engaging.

Although public speaking is definitely a skill-set that *anyone* can acquire and improve upon, public speaking competency is much more than just a set of techniques for putting together and delivering a speech. Public speaking has a venerable and impressive history traced back to the days of Aristotle over 2,500 years ago. Aristotle and scores of other scholars have devoted considerable intellectual energy to outlining the theoretical foundations of effective public speaking. Three of Aristotle's theoretical principles that are so well known that they have worked their way into our everyday vernacular are Logos, Pathos, and Ethos. Learning more about these concepts, and others, will give you the theoretical underpinnings to not only know how to give a successful speech, but an understanding about why the speech-act itself achieves its hoped-for goal.

Some of you may be approaching this course with a certain degree of fear, apprehension, or even panic. We get it. Fear of public speaking is one of the most thoroughly documented phenomena in the Speech Communication discipline. When I gave my first speech in a public speaking class at the tender age of 15, I was reduced to tears. I am not kidding you. The good news is that there are many effective techniques for dealing with your anxieties and you'll be introduced to them all in this class.

THE TEXTBOOK: Every student enrolled in *SPE 1010 Public Speaking* is expected to purchase this WORKBOOK *and* the textbook for the class, the Speaker's Compact Handbook, Fourth Edition, by Sprague, Stuart, and Bodary. Parts of this WORKBOOK are cross-referenced with the textbook.

I would like to extend my thanks to a number of people who made this workbook possible. First, Dr. William Huddy who produced a similar workbook in 2006 when he was Coordinator of the Public Speaking program at the University of Colorado at Colorado Springs. We used his workbook as the template for this workbook, and Dr. Huddy was involved in its construction from day one. I also want to thank Dr. Karen Lollar, Chair of the Department of Communication Arts and Sciences, for her support and her dedication not to micro-manage those working with her.

An important thank-you also to Ellie Moore and Travis Pemberton of Fountainhead Press, without whose expertise, knowledge, and technical support this project would not be possible.

A final word of thanks also, to you, our public speaking students, who make this course possible. I hope you have fun this semester and exit from the course with a defined path of increasing confidence in your transformation on becoming a competent public speaker.

Michael Monsour, Ph.D., Assistant Professor
SPE Coordinator of Public Speaking
Department of Communication Arts and Sciences
Metropolitan State University of Denver
wmonsour@msudenver.edu
August 1, 2015

William Huddy, Ph.D.   Michael Monsour, Ph.D.

The Field of Communication Studies and Career Opportunities

The study of communication, which can be traced back to the day of Aristotle and Plato, is a rapidly growing discipline within colleges and universities across the United States. Why? Search the "help-wanted" ads. Communication is a skill that is in high demand in a wide range of businesses and organizations, and CAS can help you achieve the communication skills necessary to succeed in today's international world of business and politics. Businesses and organizations often have their view that they can teach prospective employees the nuts and bolts of their business, BUT, they readily admit and understand that they cannot teach employees basic communication skills. They expect you to already have those skills when you enter the marketplace and apply for a job in their organization. Indeed, from the very first moment in your job interview, they will have some idea what your communication skills base is like. Communication skills are one of the most commonly listed "desired characteristics" of potential employees. "Communication skills are required." CAS can help you acquire those skills. The communication program at Metropolitan State University is designed to provide students with the practical skills and theoretical knowledge that will enable students to succeed both within and beyond the classroom. **Students interested in talking with an advisor about a major or minor in Speech Communication should call the main Speech Communication office at 303-556-3033 and ask to be scheduled for a general advising appointment.**

Students majoring or minoring in our department have a wide array of employment opportunities open to them. Communication Studies is, we believe, the broadest based and most marketable degree available on the Metro campus. A degree in Communication can open the door up to careers in broadcasting, training and development, human resources, lobbying, diversity training, organizational consulting, social work, community organizing, speech writing, mediation, public administration, and many others. Any of our students can make a cogent argument that they would be ideal for an entry level management position in almost any kind of organization.

The CAS (Communication Arts & Sciences) Department

CAS has the honored distinction of being the ONLY department on campus that specifically teaches oral communication skills. Each academic year approximately 3,000 students take SPE 1010 Public Speaking. But the Speech Communication program does much more than teach students how to give effective speeches. As hinted at earlier, our field is incredibly diverse. If a student decides to major in Speech Communication, she or he may choose an area of concentration within the department.

Listed below are the four areas of concentration and the types of jobs available for someone with that concentration. Those four areas include Broadcasting; Communication Theory; Organizational Communication; and Rhetoric and Public Address. Regardless of your concentration, the required number of Speech Communication hours is 42. The required number for our minor is 21. The minor is very flexible. Students take two required classes and then select the remaining five from all of our offerings. That way, the minor can be tailored to nicely complement your major and your career goals.

Broadcasting—(Career Options):

A graduate of Speech Communication with an emphasis in Broadcasting might aspire to careers in radio and/or television. Some of our students want to be *"in front"* of the camera or *"on-air"* as a DJ. Other students prefer to work behind the scenes on the technical side of production. Either way, our degree prepares students for a lucrative career in radio or television broadcasting.

Communication Theory—(Career Options):

A graduate of Speech Communication with an emphasis in Communication Theory is prepared for employment success in communication consulting on relationship topics, human resources, management, consulting/training, and career planning. Careers are available in education, government, politics, business, industry, and private practice as a consultant. In addition, this is an excellent program to prepare students for graduate degrees in the social services and social science research programs.

Organizational Communication—(Career Options):

A graduate of Speech Communication with an emphasis in Organizational Communication might aspire to a lucrative and satisfying career in organizational consulting/training, conference planning, workplace communication, and strategic organizational communication (*sometimes referred to as public relations*). Careers are open in government, business, non-profit organizations, industry and private consulting.

Rhetoric and Public Address—(Career Options):

A graduate of Speech Communication with an emphasis in Rhetoric and Public Address will be prepared for a wide range of employment opportunities in law, industrial and organizational communication, education administration, speech writing for political figures, teaching, and theology. From Aristotle to Martin Luther King Jr., students will learn the art of persuasion that will help them succeed in the modern world of politics, law, and administration. This concentration is ideally suited for students preparing for law school, pursuing a career in politics, or pursuing a career in education, administration, business, or politics.

Students interested in talking to an advisor about a major or minor in Speech Communication should call the main Speech Communication office at 303-556-3033 and ask to be scheduled for a general advising appointment.

A Definition: "Student Learning Outcomes"

SPE 1010 Public Speaking is a General Studies Oral Communication class. Many of you enrolled in this course are doing so in order to meet your General Studies Oral Communication requirement.

Listed below are two sets of **Student Learning Outcomes** (i.e., SLOs, what we *hope* you will learn to do by the end of the course). The first set are those that apply to all types of oral communication classes (including foreign language classes). The second set are those SLOs which are specific to SPE 1010 Public Speaking.

General Studies Student Learning Outcomes (GSSLO):

1. Demonstrate effective use of *technologies* appropriate to task and discipline.
2. Demonstrate the ability to locate sources when information is needed, and to evaluate the authenticity, validity, and reliability of resources applied for a specific purpose.
3. Create *persuasive* and well-reasoned *arguments* that are appropriate to the topic and purpose.
4. Communication in *speech* with an awareness of audience, by using language conventions appropriate to the occasion and task.
6. *Analyze* texts, sources, argumentation, identify cause and effect relationships, and recognize fallacies of argument.
7. Use and *document sources* in an ethical manner.

Specific, Measurable Student Behavioral Learning Objectives:

Upon completion of this course the student should be able to:

1. Describe the roles of speech in social and professional settings (GSSLO 1, 2).
2. Identify the differences between *spoken* and *written* discourse (GSSLO 1, 2, & 4).
3. Demonstrate competent *listening* skills (GSSLO 4).

4. Demonstrate the ability to ask questions, organize information and analyze the needs of the audience in specific speech situations (GSSLO 1, 2, 3, 4, & 6).
5. Organize topic material into a logical outline (GSSLO 2, 3, 6, & 7).
6. Construct four to seven effective speeches that demonstrate skill in research, organization, use of language, application of technology and presentation (categories include: informational, motivational, ceremonial, persuasive, technical, impromptu, and civic) (GSSLO 1, 2, 3, 4, 6, & 7).
7. Evaluate peer speeches using established criteria (GSSLO 6).
8. *Critically analyze speech* in public rhetoric (GSSLO 6 & 7).

The Eight Competencies of Public Speaking

Although effective public speaking is based on a solid theoretical foundation going back to the days of Aristotle and Cicero, it nonetheless is a skill that can be acquired and improved upon throughout one's lifetime. The National Communication Association (NCA) identified and developed 8 core public speaking competencies. These competencies were arrived at through research and testing. ***These 8 competencies are what you will be graded on throughout the semester.*** As a general guideline, each of the competencies is <u>of equal importance</u>, though at times the audience and the occasion will make some competencies more salient than others. Also, your speeches are evaluated in two broad areas: <u>Content and Delivery</u>. Competencies 1 thru 5 are content competencies. Competencies 6 thru 8 are delivery competencies.

∞ **Competency 1:**   Chooses and narrows topic appropriately for audience and occasion.

∞ **Competency 2:**   Communicates the thesis clearly in a manner appropriate for audience and occasion.

∞ **Competency 3:**   Provides supporting material (including electronic aids) appropriate to audience and occasion.

∞ **Competency 4:**   Uses an organizational pattern appropriate to audience and occasion.

∞ **Competency 5:**   Uses language appropriate to audience and occasion.

∞ **Competency 6:**   Uses vocal variety in rate, pitch, and volume to maintain interest appropriate to audience and occasion.

∞ **Competency 7:**   Uses pronunciation, grammar, and articulation appropriate to audience and occasion.

∞ **Competency 8:**   Uses physical behaviors to support the verbal message appropriate to audience and occasion.

Five Graded Speeches Given This Semester

All students in all 75 sections of SPE 1010 Public Speaking prepare and give the same five types of *graded speeches*. The reason for this is so all students taking the public speaking class have a similar and consistent experience and emerge from the class with a similar skill set. The order in which the speeches are given is left up to your individual instructor. The percentage of your semester grade that each of your five speeches is allotted is also left up to your individual instructor. The length of each of your five speeches is up to your instructor. For example, one instructor might believe that the "Persuasive" speech should be 20% of your semester grade and be a 10 minute speech, whereas a different instructor may decide that 10% is more appropriate and that the speech should only be 7 minutes long. The following brief description of each of the five speeches is presented in alphabetical order. The description of each speech type is based on your textbook.

Ceremonial Speeches: In a ceremonial speech the speaker assumes that there is a close connection among audience members who have gathered to celebrate or commemorate some important event or person. Typical speaking situations in a ceremonial context might include presenting an award, proposing a toast, giving a eulogy, or nominating a political candidate. These types of speeches are also sometimes called commemorative speeches or special occasion speeches. For more information consult Chapter 9 in your textbook.

Civic Engagement Speeches: Civic engagement speeches are special types of persuasive speeches. Although they sometime focus on "civic engagement" in politics, they are not limited to just that. Here is how an edition of the *New York Times* defined Civic Engagement, which actually reflects excerpts from *Civic Responsibility and Higher Education* published by Oryx Press:

> Civic engagement means working to make a difference in the civic life of our communities and developing the combination of knowledge, skills, values, and motivation to make that difference. It means promoting the quality of life in a community through both political and non-political processes...A morally and civically responsible individual recognizes

himself or herself as a member of a larger social fabric and therefore considers social problems to be at least partly his or her own; such an individual is willing to see the moral and civic dimensions of issues, to make and justify informed moral and civic judgments, and to take prompt action when appropriate (Ehrlich, 2000).

The three main relevant chapters in your textbook are chapters 8, 23, and 25. Some examples of civic engagement speeches are: persuading the audience about the importance of voter registration, persuading the audience to volunteer time and/or money to some community-based group, and persuading the audience to join a Youth Leadership Program with the Chamber of Commerce.

Impromptu Speeches: An impromptu speech is a "speech" given without any advance preparation. Your instructor may require a number of these during the semester since these are, by definition, short speeches (1 to 3 minutes long). All throughout your life you will be asked to "give your opinion" about something (a political candidate, an ongoing war, a controversial movie, the Broncos, your favorite place to eat, etc...). You give impromptu speeches in a wide variety of contexts: in class, at work, at a community gathering, at a friend's house. Doing this type of speaking and doing it well is A SOCIAL SKILL. As your book points out on p. 238, "An impromptu speech can, however, have elements of other types of speeches, such as a theme, planned first and last sentences, appeals to the audience, and lots of examples." Be sure to consult p. 168 in your textbook.

Informative Speeches: Some instructors may also allow you to give a speech to demonstrate (which is essentially just one of the many types of informative speeches). In a speech to inform you are NOT trying to persuade the audience of anything: you are simply presenting information that you hope they will find useful, interesting, and possibly entertaining. The information that you present needs to come from reputable sources and it needs to be understandable and well organized. The two main relevant chapters in your textbook are chapters 16 and 22.

Persuasive Speeches: In many ways, this type of speech is the most important and has certainly been studied the longest, dating back to Aristotle's analysis of logos, pathos, and ethos ("all the available means of persuasion"). In these types of speeches the speaker is trying to change one or more of the following things: attitudes of the audience towards something; beliefs the audience holds; values of the audience. So, persuasive speakers are concerned with changing the attitudes, values, and beliefs of audience members. Oftentimes, persuasive speakers also want to change the behaviors of audience members. For example, turning smokers into non-smokers, non-voters into voters, over-water users into water conservationists, atheists into Christians, etc... The four main relevant chapters in your textbook are chapters 16, 23, 24, and 25.

The Preparation Outline

For every graded speech this semester you are expected to construct a carefully thought out preparation outline. Your instructor may or may not assign a grade to this stage of the speech process. **A preparation outline is a full-sentence outline.** The preparation outline helps you to develop your speaking notes (which are key words and ideas placed on index cards that the speaker uses to speak from). Some speakers use the preparation outline to practice their speech until they are comfortable moving on to just note cards.

Preparation outlines are necessary to ensure that your speech is clearly organized and easy to follow. Studies have conclusively demonstrated that well organized speeches have more credibility with audiences than do poorly organized speeches. Well organized speeches also improve retention and comprehension on the part of the audience.

In this Workbook we provide the following example of how to construct your preparation outline. Your instructor may or may not ask you to closely follow this particular format. The textbook (pages 113-115) has the Roman Numerals as the main points of the speech. In this Workbook, we have a slightly different approach. Notice that there will be three Roman Numerals: I, II, and III. Roman Numeral I is for your Introduction. Roman Numeral II is for the Body of your speech. Roman Numeral III is the Conclusion of your speech.

Sample Outline for a Sample Informative Speech on Acid Rain

The bold-faced part of the outline is the structure you need to follow. Have each bold-faced part in your outline and then complete the outline with your own content as we have done below with the example of acid rain. For instance, the first seven parts of your skeleton outline should read: **Title of the Speech, Topic, General Purpose, Specific Purpose, Thesis Statement, Introduction, and Attention Getting Device**

Your individual instructor may require you to have a title to your speech, as we have below in this sample.

Title of the Speech: Acid Rain: No, It's Not a Jimmy Hendrix Song.

Topic: (in a full sentence state your topic, e.g., "My topic is acid rain.")

General Purpose: (in a full sentence state your general purpose, e.g., "My purpose is to inform."

Specific Purpose: (in a full sentence state your specific purpose, e.g., "I am going to inform the audience about acid rain.")

Thesis Statement: (in a full sentence state your thesis statement, the central idea, of your speech, e.g., "My central idea is that acid rain causes significant damage resulting in billions of dollars.")

I. Introduction

    a. Attention Getting Device (in a full sentence state your attention getting device)

e.g., "I will get the attention of the audience by giving the following startling statistic about acid rain…."

e.g., "I will get the attention of the audience by telling a story about acid rain."

e.g., "I will get the attention of the audience with an interesting quotation on acid rain."

    b. Thesis (in a full sentence state your central idea, e.g., "My central idea is that acid rain causes significant damage resulting in billions of dollars.")

    c. Preview Statement (in about three to six sentences state your preview statement, e.g., "In the next few minutes I will be covering three major points about acid rain. Point one is the definition of acid rain. My second point describes the places where acid rain is most likely to fall. My third point gives statistics about the financial cost of acid rain.")

    d. Transition (in a full sentence state your transition, e.g., "Now let's move on to my first point.")

II. Body

    a. First main point (in a full sentence state your first main point, e.g.," The first thing I will do is define acid rain. According to the Environmental Protection Agency, acid rain is defined as…)

        1. First subpoint (your subpoint develops your first main point)

2. Second subpoint (your subpoint develops your first main point)

Transition: (in a full sentence state the transition you will use to move from your first main point to your second main point, for example, "Now that I have defined acid rain, let's move on to my second main point.")

b. Second main point (in a full sentence state your second main point, e.g., "Acid rain falls in three primary types of locations.")

  1. First subpoint (your subpoint develops your first main point)

  2. Second subpoint (your subpoint develops your first main point)

  3. Third subpoint (your subpoint develops your first main point)

Transition: (in a full sentence state the transition you will use to move from your second main point to your third main point, for example, "Now that I have defined acid rain and described where it is most likely to fall, let's move on to my third and last main point.")

c. Third main point (in a full sentence state your third main point, e.g., "Acid rain causes significant financial damage.")

  1. First subpoint (your subpoint develops your first main point)

  2. Second subpoint (your subpoint develops your first main point)

Transition: (in a full sentence state the transition you will use to move from your third main point to the conclusion of your speech, for example, "Ok, there you have it. I have defined acid rain, described where it is most likely to fall, and given you some statistics about the tremendous amount of damage that acid rain can cause.")

III. Conclusion: See pages 184-185 in your textbook.

  a. Logical Closure (in a full sentence state how you will provide logical closure, e.g., I will provide logical closure by stating something similar to the following, "In the last few minutes I have done what I said I would do: I have defined acid rain, I have identified where it is most likely to occur, and I have given you some statistics about the financial damage caused by acid rain.")

  b. Psychological Closure (in a full sentence state how you will provide psychological closure, e.g., I will provide psychological closure by making a statement similar to the following, "I hope the information I have provided you has been useful in helping you to fill in any gaps in the knowledge that you had concerning acid harm and its harmful effects.")

       c. Clincher—In a full sentence explain what your clincher will be, e.g., "I will finish telling the story I began in the introduction" or "I will give an even more startling statistic than I began my speech with."

Class Attendance Policy

As an SPE 1010 class member you have two basic responsibilities: To give speeches and to regularly show up as an audience member to hear the speeches of your fellow classmates. Public speaking is pointless without an audience. Each of you will work really hard preparing your speech AND will be totally invested and engaged when delivering your speech. Each of you needs to demonstrate your support for one another by being a supportive audience member, and that means showing up to class. **Because of the vitally important role of attendance in a performance class, CAS has adopted the following policy regarding class attendance. This policy is the same for every section of public speaking, not just your particular class.**

1. There are NO excused absences EXCEPT for military duty, jury duty, and religious holidays. As noted in the box below, you are allowed a certain number of absences before your grade is lowered. The number of absences allowed depends upon how many times a week your class meets. Absences for military duty, jury duty, and religious holiday observances DO NOT count towards the number of absences you are allowed as long as you can provide documentation on the authenticity of your reason for missing class. *If you are going to miss a class for a religious holiday you need to inform your instructor the first week of class.*

   We were very careful in deciding how many absences you are allowed. Please do not use your allowed absences for trivial reasons. Any one of you might get sick at some point in the semester or have a work or personal emergency you must attend to. That is why we allow a certain number of absences. If you don't use up your absences for reasons like sleeping in, or going to the mountains, or just skipping classes, then IF you do get sick or have a work or family emergency, you would have absences at your disposal. If you waste your allotted absences and then need to miss more than you are allowed, your instructor will not be able to help you. If you have a true medical or family emergency, the absences allowed should be enough to get you over the hump, IF YOU DON'T WASTE YOUR ABSENCES ON TRIVIAL MATTERS. On the next page of this document you will see a breakdown of how many absences you are allowed determined by the number of times you class meets in a given week of the semester.

2. Final grades will be reduced for absences from the initial grade earned as follows:

Classes Per Week			Action
Three	**Two**	**One**	
Classes Missed	*Classes Missed*	*Classes Missed*	
6	4	2	No Grade Reduction
7	5	3	One Letter Grade Reduction
11	9	5	Two Letter Grade Reduction
15	13	7	Three Letter Grade Reduction
19	16	8	Failure to Complete Course

Grievance Procedures

The CAS SPE 1010 instructors are all carefully screened and interviewed before being hired. Each instructor has at least an M.A. degree in Communication Studies. Individual instructors are careful and fair when conducting class and assigning grades to speeches. However, in the unlikely event that you do have a problem with your instructor during the course of the semester, CAS has a grievance policy in place that you as a student must follow. This is for your protection and the protection of our instructors. Here are the steps to the policy:

1. You should send an email to your instructor and request a private meeting on campus in the CAS department office (Room 120 in the Central classroom building). In the email explain the nature of your concern. Your instructor will meet with you.

2. In the meeting with the instructor make sure you clearly articulate your concerns and make sure that you bring your class syllabus and you understand its policies. Listen to your instructor with respect, just as she/he will listen respectfully to your concerns.

3. If you are unable to work out a satisfactory resolution with your instructor and you still want to pursue the matter, inform him or her that you are taking your concerns to the SPE Coordinator, Mike Monsour.

4. Send the SPE Coordinator (me, Mike Monsour) an email requesting a meeting. I will meet with you. Before you and I meet I will have a separate meeting with your instructor. If you and I are unable to reach a satisfactory resolution you may take your concern to the Chair of the Department of Communication Arts and Sciences, Dr. Karen Lollar. If you tell me you are going to pursue this option, I will inform Dr. Lollar and your instructor.

5. Dr. Lollar will listen to your concerns. By this point in the process she has probably already spoken to me and your instructor about the situation.

6. Dr. Lollar makes the final decision regarding the situation.

Spectacular Vernacular

Being an American is about freedom of expression. Constitutional scholars, political scientists, and communication scholars and practitioners all believe that the right to speak openly and honestly without fear of repercussions is vitally important in democratic societies. In honor of our constitutional right to freedom of expression, every year in the last weekend of April the Department of Communication Arts and Sciences organizes a public speaking contest on campus. This coming April there will be four categories of events: Oratory, Water Oratory, and Extemporaneous events have a $200.00 first prize and a $100.00 second prize. The department also awards professional plaques for first and second place. All of you are eligible to compete in all events except for Faculty Oratory. Our new event, Faculty Oratory, promises to be entertaining and fun, and there will be student judges!

Registration is free and starts on March 1st, 2016. Just shoot me (Mike Monsour) an email at wmonsour@msudenver.edu and let me know which events you would like to compete in. You may enter all three events so there is a possibility of wining $600.00!

The category of "oratory" is broadly defined as a speech designed to do one or more of the following: **persuade, inspire, motivate, actuate, commemorate, celebrate, eulogize or entertain.** Contestants are free to use any topic they like. Many of our past contestants use a variation of the persuasive speech given in their SPE 1010 Public Speaking class. We encourage contestants to speak on topics such as embracing diversity, freedom of speech, civility in communication, war and peace, civic engagement, multi-cultural sensitivity, social justice, and maintaining personal space in an age of digital discourse. The category of "water oratory" is broadly defined as a speech designed to do one or more of the following: **persuade, inspire, motivate, or actuate** on some topic directly related to water issues on a local, state, national, or global level. This part of our contest is sponsored by the **OWOW** organization on campus (*One World, One Water*). The "extemp" category is a speech that contestants have 30 minutes to prepare after drawing three topics from a hat and selecting one out of the three to speak on.

For those of you who want to compete, there is help available. Once registration starts on March 1st, a number of faculty in the Department of Communication Arts and Sciences make themselves available to help students with their speeches. If you are interested in viewing actual past speeches, that is easy to do. Just get on the Metro home page and look for the "A-Z" choice at the top of the page. Click the "A to Z" in the bar at the top and then scroll down to "C" and click "Communication Arts and Sciences." Then click "Special Events," then click "Spectacular Vernacular."

Motivated Sequence

Alan Monroe of Purdue University developed Monroe's Motivated Sequence in 1934. The motivated sequence became a standard for the framing of persuasive speeches in American society, and is known for its simplicity and effectiveness in education and in debate today.

The sequence starts with an **attention getter** (similar to the way we start our Standard Preparation Outline). It transitions to the **need step**, where a speaker demonstrates to an audience why a particular thought or action is needed and should be embraced or adopted. This is followed by a **satisfaction step**, with a speaker not only demonstrating, but demonstrating in a convincing way why adoption of this thought or action will make a meaningful difference in the lives of its audience members. The **visualization step** of the sequence focuses on the art of oratory, where your analysis of the problem and analysis of the audience provides an element of persuasive power to "paint a picture" of what life will be like after this particular thought or action is adopted. And the step that perhaps most significantly defines the motivated sequence is a strong **call to action,** vocalizing to an audience that the need is so great, and the solution so worthy, that adoption of the thought or idea is an imperative. A strong call to action is viewed as so important in the context of our two persuasive speeches that we single out and provide academic points specific to the strength of this action within your speech.

Of course the use of full sentence transitions between each major segment of Monroe's Motivated Sequence is mandatory in the preparation of your outline.

Attention-Getter
(Full-Sentence Transition)
Need Step
(Full-Sentence Transition)
Satisfaction Step
(Full-Sentence Transition)
Visualization Step
(Full-Sentence Transition)
Call-To-Action

The Persuasive Speech
Public Speaking Competency Evaluation Form

(*Based on the work of the National Communication Association)

Speaker Name: _____

Date: _____

Type of Speech: _____

Competency Levels
Low/Moderate/High

1: Chooses and narrows the topic appropriate for the audience and occasion.			
2: Communicates the thesis/specific clearly and in a manner appropriate to the audience and occasion.			
3: Provides supporting materials that are appropriate to the audience and occasion (e.g., statistics, examples, expert testimony).			
4: Clear and effective organizational pattern appropriate to the audience, occasion, and the topic.			
5: Uses language that is appropriate to the audience and occasion (clear, vivid, and imaginative).			
6: Uses vocal variety in rate, pitch, and volume used to heighten and maintain interest appropriate to the audience and occasion.			
7: Uses pronunciation, grammar, and articulation appropriate to audience and occasion.			
8: Uses physical behaviors that support the verbal messages (gestures, eye contact, and use of proxemics).			

What I liked about this speech:

_____

_____

_____

_____

_____.

Public Speaking Competency Feedback and Development Form

**Highlighted items need more development

	Current level			
Organization and Content:	-	*OK*	+	++
Introduction · preview · attention getter · credibility · reason for listening				
Transitions · obvious · pause				
Organizational Pattern · clear · appropriate				
Central Idea · identifiable · focused				
Supporting Materials · smooth · names · authoritative				
Conclusion · signal end · summarize · repeat main points · closure · integrated				
Logistics · appropriate topic selection · appropriate length of speech · use of notes				
Delivery:				
Language · concrete · vivid · stories · avoid jargon				
Voice Quality · volume · rate · tone · flow				
Vocal Variety · inflection · pauses				
Kinesics · professional · energy · confident				
Eye Contact · scan · gaze · linger · inclusive				
Gestures · purposeful · integrated				
Utilization of Space · step up · step out				
Visual Aid(s):				
Design · clear · visible · professional				
Integration · smooth · purposeful				

The Persuasive Speech
Public Speaking Competency Evaluation Form
(*Based on the work of the National Communication Association)

Speaker Name: _____

Date: _____

Type of Speech: _____

	Competency Levels *Low/Moderate/High*		
1: Chooses and narrows the topic appropriate for the audience and occasion.			
2: Communicates the thesis/specific clearly and in a manner appropriate to the audience and occasion.			
3: Provides supporting materials that are appropriate to the audience and occasion (e.g., statistics, examples, expert testimony).			
4: Clear and effective organizational pattern appropriate to the audience, occasion, and the topic.			
5: Uses language that is appropriate to the audience and occasion (clear, vivid, and imaginative).			
6: Uses vocal variety in rate, pitch, and volume used to heighten and maintain interest appropriate to the audience and occasion.			
7: Uses pronunciation, grammar, and articulation appropriate to audience and occasion.			
8: Uses physical behaviors that support the verbal messages (gestures, eye contact, and use of proxemics).			

What I liked about this speech:

_____

_____

_____

_____

_____ .

Public Speaking Competency Feedback and Development Form

**Highlighted items need more development   Current level

Organization and Content:	-	OK	+	++
Introduction · preview · attention getter · credibility · reason for listening				
Transitions · obvious · pause				
Organizational Pattern · clear · appropriate				
Central Idea · identifiable · focused				
Supporting Materials · smooth · names · authoritative				
Conclusion · signal end · summarize · repeat main points · closure · integrated				
Logistics · appropriate topic selection · appropriate length of speech · use of notes				
Delivery:				
Language · concrete · vivid · stories · avoid jargon				
Voice Quality · volume · rate · tone · flow				
Vocal Variety · inflection · pauses				
Kinesics · professional · energy · confident				
Eye Contact · scan · gaze · linger · inclusive				
Gestures · purposeful · integrated				
Utilization of Space · step up · step out				
Visual Aid(s):				
Design · clear · visible · professional				
Integration · smooth · purposeful				

The Persuasive Speech
Public Speaking Competency Evaluation Form
(*Based on the work of the National Communication Association)

Speaker Name: _____

Date: _____

Type of Speech: _____

Competency Levels
Low/Moderate/High

1: Chooses and narrows the topic appropriate for the audience and occasion.			
2: Communicates the thesis/specific clearly and in a manner appropriate to the audience and occasion.			
3: Provides supporting materials that are appropriate to the audience and occasion (e.g., statistics, examples, expert testimony).			
4: Clear and effective organizational pattern appropriate to the audience, occasion, and the topic.			
5: Uses language that is appropriate to the audience and occasion (clear, vivid, and imaginative).			
6: Uses vocal variety in rate, pitch, and volume used to heighten and maintain interest appropriate to the audience and occasion.			
7: Uses pronunciation, grammar, and articulation appropriate to audience and occasion.			
8: Uses physical behaviors that support the verbal messages (gestures, eye contact, and use of proxemics).			

What I liked about this speech:

_____

_____

_____

_____

_____.

Public Speaking Competency Feedback and Development Form

**Highlighted items need more development

Organization and Content:	-	*OK*	+	++
Introduction · preview · attention getter · credibility · reason for listening				
Transitions · obvious · pause				
Organizational Pattern · clear · appropriate				
Central Idea · identifiable · focused				
Supporting Materials · smooth · names · authoritative				
Conclusion · signal end · summarize · repeat main points · closure · integrated				
Logistics · appropriate topic selection · appropriate length of speech · use of notes				
Delivery:				
Language · concrete · vivid · stories · avoid jargon				
Voice Quality · volume · rate · tone · flow				
Vocal Variety · inflection · pauses				
Kinesics · professional · energy · confident				
Eye Contact · scan · gaze · linger · inclusive				
Gestures · purposeful · integrated				
Utilization of Space · step up · step out				
Visual Aid(s):				
Design · clear · visible · professional				
Integration · smooth · purposeful				

Current level column header spans the four rating columns: - | *OK* | + | ++

The Persuasive Speech
Public Speaking Competency Evaluation Form
(*Based on the work of the National Communication Association)

Speaker Name: _____

Date: _____

Type of Speech: _____

Competency Levels
Low/Moderate/High

1: Chooses and narrows the topic appropriate for the audience and occasion.			
2: Communicates the thesis/specific clearly and in a manner appropriate to the audience and occasion.			
3: Provides supporting materials that are appropriate to the audience and occasion (e.g., statistics, examples, expert testimony).			
4: Clear and effective organizational pattern appropriate to the audience, occasion, and the topic.			
5: Uses language that is appropriate to the audience and occasion (clear, vivid, and imaginative).			
6: Uses vocal variety in rate, pitch, and volume used to heighten and maintain interest appropriate to the audience and occasion.			
7: Uses pronunciation, grammar, and articulation appropriate to audience and occasion.			
8: Uses physical behaviors that support the verbal messages (gestures, eye contact, and use of proxemics).			

What I liked about this speech:

_____
_____
_____
_____
_____.

Name _____

Public Speaking Competency Feedback and Development Form

**Highlighted items need more development

	Current level			
Organization and Content:	-	*OK*	+	++
Introduction · preview · attention getter · credibility · reason for listening				
Transitions · obvious · pause				
Organizational Pattern · clear · appropriate				
Central Idea · identifiable · focused				
Supporting Materials · smooth · names · authoritative				
Conclusion · signal end · summarize · repeat main points · closure · integrated				
Logistics · appropriate topic selection · appropriate length of speech · use of notes				
Delivery:				
Language · concrete · vivid · stories · avoid jargon				
Voice Quality · volume · rate · tone · flow				
Vocal Variety · inflection · pauses				
Kinesics · professional · energy · confident				
Eye Contact · scan · gaze · linger · inclusive				
Gestures · purposeful · integrated				
Utilization of Space · step up · step out				
Visual Aid(s):				
Design · clear · visible · professional				
Integration · smooth · purposeful				

The Persuasive Speech
Public Speaking Competency Evaluation Form
(*Based on the work of the National Communication Association)

Speaker Name: _____

Date: _____

Type of Speech: _____

	Competency Levels Low/Moderate/High		
1: Chooses and narrows the topic appropriate for the audience and occasion.			
2: Communicates the thesis/specific clearly and in a manner appropriate to the audience and occasion.			
3: Provides supporting materials that are appropriate to the audience and occasion (e.g., statistics, examples, expert testimony).			
4: Clear and effective organizational pattern appropriate to the audience, occasion, and the topic.			
5: Uses language that is appropriate to the audience and occasion (clear, vivid, and imaginative).			
6: Uses vocal variety in rate, pitch, and volume used to heighten and maintain interest appropriate to the audience and occasion.			
7: Uses pronunciation, grammar, and articulation appropriate to audience and occasion.			
8: Uses physical behaviors that support the verbal messages (gestures, eye contact, and use of proxemics).			

What I liked about this speech:

_____

_____

_____

_____

_____.

Public Speaking Competency Feedback and Development Form

**Highlighted items need more development	Current level			
Organization and Content:	-	*OK*	+	++
Introduction · preview · attention getter · credibility · reason for listening				
Transitions · obvious · pause				
Organizational Pattern · clear · appropriate				
Central Idea · identifiable · focused				
Supporting Materials · smooth · names · authoritative				
Conclusion · signal end · summarize · repeat main points · closure · integrated				
Logistics · appropriate topic selection · appropriate length of speech · use of notes				
Delivery:				
Language · concrete · vivid · stories · avoid jargon				
Voice Quality · volume · rate · tone · flow				
Vocal Variety · inflection · pauses				
Kinesics · professional · energy · confident				
Eye Contact · scan · gaze · linger · inclusive				
Gestures · purposeful · integrated				
Utilization of Space · step up · step out				
Visual Aid(s):				
Design · clear · visible · professional				
Integration · smooth · purposeful				

The Persuasive Speech
Public Speaking Competency Evaluation Form
(*Based on the work of the National Communication Association)

Speaker Name: _____

Date: _____

Type of Speech: _____

Competency Levels
Low/Moderate/High

1: Chooses and narrows the topic appropriate for the audience and occasion.			
2: Communicates the thesis/specific clearly and in a manner appropriate to the audience and occasion.			
3: Provides supporting materials that are appropriate to the audience and occasion (e.g., statistics, examples, expert testimony).			
4: Clear and effective organizational pattern appropriate to the audience, occasion, and the topic.			
5: Uses language that is appropriate to the audience and occasion (clear, vivid, and imaginative).			
6: Uses vocal variety in rate, pitch, and volume used to heighten and maintain interest appropriate to the audience and occasion.			
7: Uses pronunciation, grammar, and articulation appropriate to audience and occasion.			
8: Uses physical behaviors that support the verbal messages (gestures, eye contact, and use of proxemics).			

What I liked about this speech:

_____
_____
_____
_____
_____.

Public Speaking Competency Feedback and Development Form

**Highlighted items need more development

**Highlighted items need more development	Current level			
Organization and Content:	-	*OK*	+	++
Introduction · preview · attention getter · credibility · reason for listening				
Transitions · obvious · pause				
Organizational Pattern · clear · appropriate				
Central Idea · identifiable · focused				
Supporting Materials · smooth · names · authoritative				
Conclusion · signal end · summarize · repeat main points · closure · integrated				
Logistics · appropriate topic selection · appropriate length of speech · use of notes				
Delivery:				
Language · concrete · vivid · stories · avoid jargon				
Voice Quality · volume · rate · tone · flow				
Vocal Variety · inflection · pauses				
Kinesics · professional · energy · confident				
Eye Contact · scan · gaze · linger · inclusive				
Gestures · purposeful · integrated				
Utilization of Space · step up · step out				
Visual Aid(s):				
Design · clear · visible · professional				
Integration · smooth · purposeful				

The Persuasive Speech
Public Speaking Competency Evaluation Form
(*Based on the work of the National Communication Association)

Speaker Name: _____

Date: _____

Type of Speech: _____

Competency Levels
Low/Moderate/High

1: Chooses and narrows the topic appropriate for the audience and occasion.			
2: Communicates the thesis/specific clearly and in a manner appropriate to the audience and occasion.			
3: Provides supporting materials that are appropriate to the audience and occasion (e.g., statistics, examples, expert testimony).			
4: Clear and effective organizational pattern appropriate to the audience, occasion, and the topic.			
5: Uses language that is appropriate to the audience and occasion (clear, vivid, and imaginative).			
6: Uses vocal variety in rate, pitch, and volume used to heighten and maintain interest appropriate to the audience and occasion.			
7: Uses pronunciation, grammar, and articulation appropriate to audience and occasion.			
8: Uses physical behaviors that support the verbal messages (gestures, eye contact, and use of proxemics).			

What I liked about this speech:

_____

_____

_____

_____

_____.

Name _____

Public Speaking Competency Feedback and Development Form

**Highlighted items need more development

	Current level			
Organization and Content:	-	*OK*	+	++
Introduction · preview · attention getter · credibility · reason for listening				
Transitions · obvious · pause				
Organizational Pattern · clear · appropriate				
Central Idea · identifiable · focused				
Supporting Materials · smooth · names · authoritative				
Conclusion · signal end · summarize · repeat main points · closure · integrated				
Logistics · appropriate topic selection · appropriate length of speech · use of notes				
Delivery:				
Language · concrete · vivid · stories · avoid jargon				
Voice Quality · volume · rate · tone · flow				
Vocal Variety · inflection · pauses				
Kinesics · professional · energy · confident				
Eye Contact · scan · gaze · linger · inclusive				
Gestures · purposeful · integrated				
Utilization of Space · step up · step out				
Visual Aid(s):				
Design · clear · visible · professional				
Integration · smooth · purposeful				

The Persuasive Speech
Public Speaking Competency Evaluation Form
(*Based on the work of the National Communication Association)

Speaker Name: _____

Date: _____

Type of Speech: _____

Competency Levels
Low/Moderate/High

1: Chooses and narrows the topic appropriate for the audience and occasion.			
2: Communicates the thesis/specific clearly and in a manner appropriate to the audience and occasion.			
3: Provides supporting materials that are appropriate to the audience and occasion (e.g., statistics, examples, expert testimony).			
4: Clear and effective organizational pattern appropriate to the audience, occasion, and the topic.			
5: Uses language that is appropriate to the audience and occasion (clear, vivid, and imaginative).			
6: Uses vocal variety in rate, pitch, and volume used to heighten and maintain interest appropriate to the audience and occasion.			
7: Uses pronunciation, grammar, and articulation appropriate to audience and occasion.			
8: Uses physical behaviors that support the verbal messages (gestures, eye contact, and use of proxemics).			

What I liked about this speech:

_____

_____

_____

_____

_____.

Name _____

Public Speaking Competency Feedback and Development Form

**Highlighted items need more development Current level

Organization and Content:	-	OK	+	++
Introduction · preview · attention getter · credibility · reason for listening				
Transitions · obvious · pause				
Organizational Pattern · clear · appropriate				
Central Idea · identifiable · focused				
Supporting Materials · smooth · names · authoritative				
Conclusion · signal end · summarize · repeat main points · closure · integrated				
Logistics · appropriate topic selection · appropriate length of speech · use of notes				
Delivery:				
Language · concrete · vivid · stories · avoid jargon				
Voice Quality · volume · rate · tone · flow				
Vocal Variety · inflection · pauses				
Kinesics · professional · energy · confident				
Eye Contact · scan · gaze · linger · inclusive				
Gestures · purposeful · integrated				
Utilization of Space · step up · step out				
Visual Aid(s):				
Design · clear · visible · professional				
Integration · smooth · purposeful				

The Persuasive Speech
Public Speaking Competency Evaluation Form
(*Based on the work of the National Communication Association)

Speaker Name: _____

Date: _____

Type of Speech: _____

Competency Levels
Low/Moderate/High

	Low	Moderate	High
1: Chooses and narrows the topic appropriate for the audience and occasion.			
2: Communicates the thesis/specific clearly and in a manner appropriate to the audience and occasion.			
3: Provides supporting materials that are appropriate to the audience and occasion (e.g., statistics, examples, expert testimony).			
4: Clear and effective organizational pattern appropriate to the audience, occasion, and the topic.			
5: Uses language that is appropriate to the audience and occasion (clear, vivid, and imaginative).			
6: Uses vocal variety in rate, pitch, and volume used to heighten and maintain interest appropriate to the audience and occasion.			
7: Uses pronunciation, grammar, and articulation appropriate to audience and occasion.			
8: Uses physical behaviors that support the verbal messages (gestures, eye contact, and use of proxemics).			

What I liked about this speech:

_____

_____

_____

_____

_____ .

Name _____

Public Speaking Competency Feedback and Development Form

**Highlighted items need more development   Current level

Organization and Content:	-	OK	+	++
Introduction · preview · attention getter · credibility · reason for listening				
Transitions · obvious · pause				
Organizational Pattern · clear · appropriate				
Central Idea · identifiable · focused				
Supporting Materials · smooth · names · authoritative				
Conclusion · signal end · summarize · repeat main points · closure · integrated				
Logistics · appropriate topic selection · appropriate length of speech · use of notes				
Delivery:				
Language · concrete · vivid · stories · avoid jargon				
Voice Quality · volume · rate · tone · flow				
Vocal Variety · inflection · pauses				
Kinesics · professional · energy · confident				
Eye Contact · scan · gaze · linger · inclusive				
Gestures · purposeful · integrated				
Utilization of Space · step up · step out				
Visual Aid(s):				
Design · clear · visible · professional				
Integration · smooth · purposeful				

The Persuasive Speech
Public Speaking Competency Evaluation Form
(*Based on the work of the National Communication Association)

Speaker Name: _____

Date: _____

Type of Speech: _____

	Competency Levels Low/Moderate/High		
1: Chooses and narrows the topic appropriate for the audience and occasion.			
2: Communicates the thesis/specific clearly and in a manner appropriate to the audience and occasion.			
3: Provides supporting materials that are appropriate to the audience and occasion (e.g., statistics, examples, expert testimony).			
4: Clear and effective organizational pattern appropriate to the audience, occasion, and the topic.			
5: Uses language that is appropriate to the audience and occasion (clear, vivid, and imaginative).			
6: Uses vocal variety in rate, pitch, and volume used to heighten and maintain interest appropriate to the audience and occasion.			
7: Uses pronunciation, grammar, and articulation appropriate to audience and occasion.			
8: Uses physical behaviors that support the verbal messages (gestures, eye contact, and use of proxemics).			

What I liked about this speech:

_____

_____

_____

_____

_____.

Public Speaking Competency Feedback and Development Form

**Highlighted items need more development

Organization and Content:	-	OK	+	++
Introduction · preview · attention getter · credibility · reason for listening				
Transitions · obvious · pause				
Organizational Pattern · clear · appropriate				
Central Idea · identifiable · focused				
Supporting Materials · smooth · names · authoritative				
Conclusion · signal end · summarize · repeat main points · closure · integrated				
Logistics · appropriate topic selection · appropriate length of speech · use of notes				
Delivery:				
Language · concrete · vivid · stories · avoid jargon				
Voice Quality · volume · rate · tone · flow				
Vocal Variety · inflection · pauses				
Kinesics · professional · energy · confident				
Eye Contact · scan · gaze · linger · inclusive				
Gestures · purposeful · integrated				
Utilization of Space · step up · step out				
Visual Aid(s):				
Design · clear · visible · professional				
Integration · smooth · purposeful				

The header row "Current level" spans the columns **-**, **OK**, **+**, **++**.

The Informative Speech
Public Speaking Competency Evaluation Form
(*Based on the work of the National Communication Association)

Speaker Name: _____

Date: _____

Type of Speech: _____

Competency Levels
Low/Moderate/High

	Low	Moderate	High
1: Chooses and narrows the topic appropriate for the audience and occasion.			
2: Communicates the thesis/specific clearly and in a manner appropriate to the audience and occasion.			
3: Provides supporting materials that are appropriate to the audience and occasion (e.g., statistics, examples, expert testimony).			
4: Clear and effective organizational pattern appropriate to the audience, occasion, and the topic.			
5: Uses language that is appropriate to the audience and occasion (clear, vivid, and imaginative).			
6: Uses vocal variety in rate, pitch, and volume used to heighten and maintain interest appropriate to the audience and occasion.			
7: Uses pronunciation, grammar, and articulation appropriate to the audience and occasion.			
8: Uses physical behaviors that support the verbal messages (gestures, eye contact, and use of proxemics).			

What I liked about this speech:

_____

_____

_____

_____

_____.

Name _____

Public Speaking Competency Feedback and Development Form

**Highlighted items need more development

	Current level			
Organization and Content:	-	*OK*	+	++
Introduction · preview · attention getter · credibility · reason for listening				
Transitions · obvious · pause				
Organizational Pattern · clear · appropriate				
Central Idea · identifiable · focused				
Supporting Materials · smooth · names · authoritative				
Conclusion · signal end · summarize · repeat main points · closure · integrated				
Logistics · appropriate topic selection · appropriate length of speech · use of notes				
Delivery:				
Language · concrete · vivid · stories · avoid jargon				
Voice Quality · volume · rate · tone · flow				
Vocal Variety · inflection · pauses				
Kinesics · professional · energy · confident				
Eye Contact · scan · gaze · linger · inclusive				
Gestures · purposeful · integrated				
Utilization of Space · step up · step out				
Visual Aid(s):				
Design · clear · visible · professional				
Integration · smooth · purposeful				

The Informative Speech
Public Speaking Competency Evaluation Form
(*Based on the work of the National Communication Association)

Speaker Name: _____

Date: _____

Type of Speech: _____

	Competency Levels *Low/Moderate/High*		
1: Chooses and narrows the topic appropriate for the audience and occasion.			
2: Communicates the thesis/specific clearly and in a manner appropriate to the audience and occasion.			
3: Provides supporting materials that are appropriate to the audience and occasion (e.g., statistics, examples, expert testimony).			
4: Clear and effective organizational pattern appropriate to the audience, occasion, and the topic.			
5: Uses language that is appropriate to the audience and occasion (clear, vivid, and imaginative).			
6: Uses vocal variety in rate, pitch, and volume used to heighten and maintain interest appropriate to the audience and occasion.			
7: Uses pronunciation, grammar, and articulation appropriate to the audience and occasion.			
8: Uses physical behaviors that support the verbal messages (gestures, eye contact, and use of proxemics).			

What I liked about this speech:

_____

_____

_____

_____

_____.

Name ____________________

Public Speaking Competency Feedback and Development Form

**Highlighted items need more development

	Current level			
Organization and Content:	-	*OK*	+	++
Introduction · preview · attention getter · credibility · reason for listening				
Transitions · obvious · pause				
Organizational Pattern · clear · appropriate				
Central Idea · identifiable · focused				
Supporting Materials · smooth · names · authoritative				
Conclusion · signal end · summarize · repeat main points · closure · integrated				
Logistics · appropriate topic selection · appropriate length of speech · use of notes				
Delivery:				
Language · concrete · vivid · stories · avoid jargon				
Voice Quality · volume · rate · tone · flow				
Vocal Variety · inflection · pauses				
Kinesics · professional · energy · confident				
Eye Contact · scan · gaze · linger · inclusive				
Gestures · purposeful · integrated				
Utilization of Space · step up · step out				
Visual Aid(s):				
Design · clear · visible · professional				
Integration · smooth · purposeful				

The Informative Speech
Public Speaking Competency Evaluation Form
(*Based on the work of the National Communication Association)

Speaker Name: _____

Date: _____

Type of Speech: _____

Competency Levels
Low/Moderate/High

	Low	Moderate	High
1: Chooses and narrows the topic appropriate for the audience and occasion.			
2: Communicates the thesis/specific clearly and in a manner appropriate to the audience and occasion.			
3: Provides supporting materials that are appropriate to the audience and occasion (e.g., statistics, examples, expert testimony).			
4: Clear and effective organizational pattern appropriate to the audience, occasion, and the topic.			
5: Uses language that is appropriate to the audience and occasion (clear, vivid, and imaginative).			
6: Uses vocal variety in rate, pitch, and volume used to heighten and maintain interest appropriate to the audience and occasion.			
7: Uses pronunciation, grammar, and articulation appropriate to the audience and occasion.			
8: Uses physical behaviors that support the verbal messages (gestures, eye contact, and use of proxemics).			

What I liked about this speech:

_____

_____

_____

_____

_____.

Name _____

Public Speaking Competency Feedback and Development Form

**Highlighted items need more development

Organization and Content:	-	*OK*	+	++
Introduction · preview · attention getter · credibility · reason for listening				
Transitions · obvious · pause				
Organizational Pattern · clear · appropriate				
Central Idea · identifiable · focused				
Supporting Materials · smooth · names · authoritative				
Conclusion · signal end · summarize · repeat main points · closure · integrated				
Logistics · appropriate topic selection · appropriate length of speech · use of notes				
Delivery:				
Language · concrete · vivid · stories · avoid jargon				
Voice Quality · volume · rate · tone · flow				
Vocal Variety · inflection · pauses				
Kinesics · professional · energy · confident				
Eye Contact · scan · gaze · linger · inclusive				
Gestures · purposeful · integrated				
Utilization of Space · step up · step out				
Visual Aid(s):				
Design · clear · visible · professional				
Integration · smooth · purposeful				

Current level appears above the four rating columns (-, *OK*, +, ++).

The Informative Speech
Public Speaking Competency Evaluation Form
(*Based on the work of the National Communication Association)

Speaker Name: _____

Date: _____

Type of Speech: _____

Competency Levels
Low/Moderate/High

1: Chooses and narrows the topic appropriate for the audience and occasion.			
2: Communicates the thesis/specific clearly and in a manner appropriate to the audience and occasion.			
3: Provides supporting materials that are appropriate to the audience and occasion (e.g., statistics, examples, expert testimony).			
4: Clear and effective organizational pattern appropriate to the audience, occasion, and the topic.			
5: Uses language that is appropriate to the audience and occasion (clear, vivid, and imaginative).			
6: Uses vocal variety in rate, pitch, and volume used to heighten and maintain interest appropriate to the audience and occasion.			
7: Uses pronunciation, grammar, and articulation appropriate to the audience and occasion.			
8: Uses physical behaviors that support the verbal messages (gestures, eye contact, and use of proxemics).			

What I liked about this speech:

_____

_____

_____

_____

_____.

Public Speaking Competency Feedback and Development Form

**Highlighted items need more development	Current level			
Organization and Content:	-	*OK*	+	++
Introduction · preview · attention getter · credibility · reason for listening				
Transitions · obvious · pause				
Organizational Pattern · clear · appropriate				
Central Idea · identifiable · focused				
Supporting Materials · smooth · names · authoritative				
Conclusion · signal end · summarize · repeat main points · closure · integrated				
Logistics · appropriate topic selection · appropriate length of speech · use of notes				
Delivery:				
Language · concrete · vivid · stories · avoid jargon				
Voice Quality · volume · rate · tone · flow				
Vocal Variety · inflection · pauses				
Kinesics · professional · energy · confident				
Eye Contact · scan · gaze · linger · inclusive				
Gestures · purposeful · integrated				
Utilization of Space · step up · step out				
Visual Aid(s):				
Design · clear · visible · professional				
Integration · smooth · purposeful				

The Informative Speech
Public Speaking Competency Evaluation Form
(*Based on the work of the National Communication Association)

Speaker Name: _____

Date: _____

Type of Speech: _____

Competency Levels
Low/Moderate/High

	Low	Moderate	High
1: Chooses and narrows the topic appropriate for the audience and occasion.			
2: Communicates the thesis/specific clearly and in a manner appropriate to the audience and occasion.			
3: Provides supporting materials that are appropriate to the audience and occasion (e.g., statistics, examples, expert testimony).			
4: Clear and effective organizational pattern appropriate to the audience, occasion, and the topic.			
5: Uses language that is appropriate to the audience and occasion (clear, vivid, and imaginative).			
6: Uses vocal variety in rate, pitch, and volume used to heighten and maintain interest appropriate to the audience and occasion.			
7: Uses pronunciation, grammar, and articulation appropriate to the audience and occasion.			
8: Uses physical behaviors that support the verbal messages (gestures, eye contact, and use of proxemics).			

What I liked about this speech:

_____
_____
_____
_____
_____.

Public Speaking Competency Feedback and Development Form

**Highlighted items need more development

	Current level			
Organization and Content:	-	*OK*	+	++
Introduction · preview · attention getter · credibility · reason for listening				
Transitions · obvious · pause				
Organizational Pattern · clear · appropriate				
Central Idea · identifiable · focused				
Supporting Materials · smooth · names · authoritative				
Conclusion · signal end · summarize · repeat main points · closure · integrated				
Logistics · appropriate topic selection · appropriate length of speech · use of notes				
Delivery:				
Language · concrete · vivid · stories · avoid jargon				
Voice Quality · volume · rate · tone · flow				
Vocal Variety · inflection · pauses				
Kinesics · professional · energy · confident				
Eye Contact · scan · gaze · linger · inclusive				
Gestures · purposeful · integrated				
Utilization of Space · step up · step out				
Visual Aid(s):				
Design · clear · visible · professional				
Integration · smooth · purposeful				

The Informative Speech
Public Speaking Competency Evaluation Form
(*Based on the work of the National Communication Association)

Speaker Name: _____

Date: _____

Type of Speech: _____

Competency Levels
Low/Moderate/High

	Low	Moderate	High
1: Chooses and narrows the topic appropriate for the audience and occasion.			
2: Communicates the thesis/specific clearly and in a manner appropriate to the audience and occasion.			
3: Provides supporting materials that are appropriate to the audience and occasion (e.g., statistics, examples, expert testimony).			
4: Clear and effective organizational pattern appropriate to the audience, occasion, and the topic.			
5: Uses language that is appropriate to the audience and occasion (clear, vivid, and imaginative).			
6: Uses vocal variety in rate, pitch, and volume used to heighten and maintain interest appropriate to the audience and occasion.			
7: Uses pronunciation, grammar, and articulation appropriate to the audience and occasion.			
8: Uses physical behaviors that support the verbal messages (gestures, eye contact, and use of proxemics).			

What I liked about this speech:

_____

_____

_____

_____

_____.

Name _____

Public Speaking Competency Feedback and Development Form

**Highlighted items need more development   Current level

Organization and Content:	-	*OK*	+	++
Introduction · preview · attention getter · credibility · reason for listening				
Transitions · obvious · pause				
Organizational Pattern · clear · appropriate				
Central Idea · identifiable · focused				
Supporting Materials · smooth · names · authoritative				
Conclusion · signal end · summarize · repeat main points · closure · integrated				
Logistics · appropriate topic selection · appropriate length of speech · use of notes				
Delivery:				
Language · concrete · vivid · stories · avoid jargon				
Voice Quality · volume · rate · tone · flow				
Vocal Variety · inflection · pauses				
Kinesics · professional · energy · confident				
Eye Contact · scan · gaze · linger · inclusive				
Gestures · purposeful · integrated				
Utilization of Space · step up · step out				
Visual Aid(s):				
Design · clear · visible · professional				
Integration · smooth · purposeful				

The Informative Speech
Public Speaking Competency Evaluation Form
(*Based on the work of the National Communication Association)

Speaker Name: _____

Date: _____

Type of Speech: _____

Competency Levels
Low/Moderate/High

1: Chooses and narrows the topic appropriate for the audience and occasion.			
2: Communicates the thesis/specific clearly and in a manner appropriate to the audience and occasion.			
3: Provides supporting materials that are appropriate to the audience and occasion (e.g., statistics, examples, expert testimony).			
4: Clear and effective organizational pattern appropriate to the audience, occasion, and the topic.			
5: Uses language that is appropriate to the audience and occasion (clear, vivid, and imaginative).			
6: Uses vocal variety in rate, pitch, and volume used to heighten and maintain interest appropriate to the audience and occasion.			
7: Uses pronunciation, grammar, and articulation appropriate to the audience and occasion.			
8: Uses physical behaviors that support the verbal messages (gestures, eye contact, and use of proxemics).			

What I liked about this speech:

_____

_____

_____

_____

_____.

Name _____

Public Speaking Competency Feedback and Development Form

**Highlighted items need more development

**Highlighted items need more development	Current level			
Organization and Content:	-	*OK*	+	++
Introduction · preview · attention getter · credibility · reason for listening				
Transitions · obvious · pause				
Organizational Pattern · clear · appropriate				
Central Idea · identifiable · focused				
Supporting Materials · smooth · names · authoritative				
Conclusion · signal end · summarize · repeat main points · closure · integrated				
Logistics · appropriate topic selection · appropriate length of speech · use of notes				
Delivery:				
Language · concrete · vivid · stories · avoid jargon				
Voice Quality · volume · rate · tone · flow				
Vocal Variety · inflection · pauses				
Kinesics · professional · energy · confident				
Eye Contact · scan · gaze · linger · inclusive				
Gestures · purposeful · integrated				
Utilization of Space · step up · step out				
Visual Aid(s):				
Design · clear · visible · professional				
Integration · smooth · purposeful				

The Informative Speech
Public Speaking Competency Evaluation Form
(*Based on the work of the National Communication Association)

Speaker Name: _____

Date: _____

Type of Speech: _____

Competency Levels
Low/Moderate/High

1: Chooses and narrows the topic appropriate for the audience and occasion.			
2: Communicates the thesis/specific clearly and in a manner appropriate to the audience and occasion.			
3: Provides supporting materials that are appropriate to the audience and occasion (e.g., statistics, examples, expert testimony).			
4: Clear and effective organizational pattern appropriate to the audience, occasion, and the topic.			
5: Uses language that is appropriate to the audience and occasion (clear, vivid, and imaginative).			
6: Uses vocal variety in rate, pitch, and volume used to heighten and maintain interest appropriate to the audience and occasion.			
7: Uses pronunciation, grammar, and articulation appropriate to the audience and occasion.			
8: Uses physical behaviors that support the verbal messages (gestures, eye contact, and use of proxemics).			

What I liked about this speech:

_____

_____

_____

_____

_____.

Name _____

Public Speaking Competency Feedback and Development Form

**Highlighted items need more development

	Current level			
Organization and Content:	-	*OK*	+	++
Introduction · preview · attention getter · credibility · reason for listening				
Transitions · obvious · pause				
Organizational Pattern · clear · appropriate				
Central Idea · identifiable · focused				
Supporting Materials · smooth · names · authoritative				
Conclusion · signal end · summarize · repeat main points · closure · integrated				
Logistics · appropriate topic selection · appropriate length of speech · use of notes				
Delivery:				
Language · concrete · vivid · stories · avoid jargon				
Voice Quality · volume · rate · tone · flow				
Vocal Variety · inflection · pauses				
Kinesics · professional · energy · confident				
Eye Contact · scan · gaze · linger · inclusive				
Gestures · purposeful · integrated				
Utilization of Space · step up · step out				
Visual Aid(s):				
Design · clear · visible · professional				
Integration · smooth · purposeful				

The Informative Speech
Public Speaking Competency Evaluation Form
(*Based on the work of the National Communication Association)

Speaker Name: _____

Date: _____

Type of Speech: _____

	Low	Moderate	High
1: Chooses and narrows the topic appropriate for the audience and occasion.			
2: Communicates the thesis/specific clearly and in a manner appropriate to the audience and occasion.			
3: Provides supporting materials that are appropriate to the audience and occasion (e.g., statistics, examples, expert testimony).			
4: Clear and effective organizational pattern appropriate to the audience, occasion, and the topic.			
5: Uses language that is appropriate to the audience and occasion (clear, vivid, and imaginative).			
6: Uses vocal variety in rate, pitch, and volume used to heighten and maintain interest appropriate to the audience and occasion.			
7: Uses pronunciation, grammar, and articulation appropriate to the audience and occasion.			
8: Uses physical behaviors that support the verbal messages (gestures, eye contact, and use of proxemics).			

What I liked about this speech:

_____

_____

_____

_____

_____.

Public Speaking Competency Feedback and Development Form

**Highlighted items need more development

**Highlighted items need more development	Current level			
Organization and Content:	-	*OK*	+	++
Introduction · preview · attention getter · credibility · reason for listening				
Transitions · obvious · pause				
Organizational Pattern · clear · appropriate				
Central Idea · identifiable · focused				
Supporting Materials · smooth · names · authoritative				
Conclusion · signal end · summarize · repeat main points · closure · integrated				
Logistics · appropriate topic selection · appropriate length of speech · use of notes				
Delivery:				
Language · concrete · vivid · stories · avoid jargon				
Voice Quality · volume · rate · tone · flow				
Vocal Variety · inflection · pauses				
Kinesics · professional · energy · confident				
Eye Contact · scan · gaze · linger · inclusive				
Gestures · purposeful · integrated				
Utilization of Space · step up · step out				
Visual Aid(s):				
Design · clear · visible · professional				
Integration · smooth · purposeful				

The Informative Speech
Public Speaking Competency Evaluation Form
(*Based on the work of the National Communication Association)

Speaker Name: _____

Date: _____

Type of Speech: _____

Competency Levels
Low/Moderate/High

	Low	Moderate	High
1: Chooses and narrows the topic appropriate for the audience and occasion.			
2: Communicates the thesis/specific clearly and in a manner appropriate to the audience and occasion.			
3: Provides supporting materials that are appropriate to the audience and occasion (e.g., statistics, examples, expert testimony).			
4: Clear and effective organizational pattern appropriate to the audience, occasion, and the topic.			
5: Uses language that is appropriate to the audience and occasion (clear, vivid, and imaginative).			
6: Uses vocal variety in rate, pitch, and volume used to heighten and maintain interest appropriate to the audience and occasion.			
7: Uses pronunciation, grammar, and articulation appropriate to the audience and occasion.			
8: Uses physical behaviors that support the verbal messages (gestures, eye contact, and use of proxemics).			

What I liked about this speech:

_____

_____

_____

_____

_____ .

Name _____

Public Speaking Competency Feedback and Development Form

**Highlighted items need more development

	Current level			
Organization and Content:	-	*OK*	+	++
Introduction · preview · attention getter · credibility · reason for listening				
Transitions · obvious · pause				
Organizational Pattern · clear · appropriate				
Central Idea · identifiable · focused				
Supporting Materials · smooth · names · authoritative				
Conclusion · signal end · summarize · repeat main points · closure · integrated				
Logistics · appropriate topic selection · appropriate length of speech · use of notes				
Delivery:				
Language · concrete · vivid · stories · avoid jargon				
Voice Quality · volume · rate · tone · flow				
Vocal Variety · inflection · pauses				
Kinesics · professional · energy · confident				
Eye Contact · scan · gaze · linger · inclusive				
Gestures · purposeful · integrated				
Utilization of Space · step up · step out				
Visual Aid(s):				
Design · clear · visible · professional				
Integration · smooth · purposeful				

The Civic Engagement Speech
Public Speaking Competency Evaluation Form
(*Based on the work of the National Communication Association)

Speaker Name: _____

Date: _____

Type of Speech: _____

Competency Levels
Low/Moderate/High

	Low	Moderate	High
1: Chooses and narrows the topic appropriate for the audience and occasion.			
2: Communicates the thesis/specific clearly and in a manner appropriate to the audience and occasion.			
3: Provides supporting materials that are appropriate to the audience and occasion (e.g., statistics, examples, expert testimony).			
4: Clear and effective organizational pattern appropriate to the audience, occasion, and the topic.			
5: Uses language that is appropriate to the audience and occasion (clear, vivid, and imaginative).			
6: Uses vocal variety in rate, pitch, and volume used to heighten and maintain interest appropriate to the audience and occasion.			
7: Uses pronunciation, grammar, and articulation appropriate to the audience and occasion.			
8: Uses physical behaviors that support the verbal messages (gestures, eye contact, and use of proxemics).			

What I liked about this speech:

_____

_____

_____

_____

_____ .

Name _____

Public Speaking Competency Feedback and Development Form

**Highlighted items need more development

	Current level			
Organization and Content:	-	*OK*	+	++
Introduction · preview · attention getter · credibility · reason for listening				
Transitions · obvious · pause				
Organizational Pattern · clear · appropriate				
Central Idea · identifiable · focused				
Supporting Materials · smooth · names · authoritative				
Conclusion · signal end · summarize · repeat main points · closure · integrated				
Logistics · appropriate topic selection · appropriate length of speech · use of notes				
Delivery:				
Language · concrete · vivid · stories · avoid jargon				
Voice Quality · volume · rate · tone · flow				
Vocal Variety · inflection · pauses				
Kinesics · professional · energy · confident				
Eye Contact · scan · gaze · linger · inclusive				
Gestures · purposeful · integrated				
Utilization of Space · step up · step out				
Visual Aid(s):				
Design · clear · visible · professional				
Integration · smooth · purposeful				

The Civic Engagement Speech
Public Speaking Competency Evaluation Form

(*Based on the work of the National Communication Association)

Speaker Name: _____

Date: _____

Type of Speech: _____

Competency Levels

Low/Moderate/High

1: Chooses and narrows the topic appropriate for the audience and occasion.			
2: Communicates the thesis/specific clearly and in a manner appropriate to the audience and occasion.			
3: Provides supporting materials that are appropriate to the audience and occasion (e.g., statistics, examples, expert testimony).			
4: Clear and effective organizational pattern appropriate to the audience, occasion, and the topic.			
5: Uses language that is appropriate to the audience and occasion (clear, vivid, and imaginative).			
6: Uses vocal variety in rate, pitch, and volume used to heighten and maintain interest appropriate to the audience and occasion.			
7: Uses pronunciation, grammar, and articulation appropriate to the audience and occasion.			
8: Uses physical behaviors that support the verbal messages (gestures, eye contact, and use of proxemics).			

What I liked about this speech:

_____

_____

_____

_____

_____.

Name _____

Public Speaking Competency Feedback and Development Form

**Highlighted items need more development

Current level

	-	*OK*	+	++
Organization and Content:				
Introduction · preview · attention getter · credibility · reason for listening				
Transitions · obvious · pause				
Organizational Pattern · clear · appropriate				
Central Idea · identifiable · focused				
Supporting Materials · smooth · names · authoritative				
Conclusion · signal end · summarize · repeat main points · closure · integrated				
Logistics · appropriate topic selection · appropriate length of speech · use of notes				
Delivery:				
Language · concrete · vivid · stories · avoid jargon				
Voice Quality · volume · rate · tone · flow				
Vocal Variety · inflection · pauses				
Kinesics · professional · energy · confident				
Eye Contact · scan · gaze · linger · inclusive				
Gestures · purposeful · integrated				
Utilization of Space · step up · step out				
Visual Aid(s):				
Design · clear · visible · professional				
Integration · smooth · purposeful				

The Civic Engagement Speech
Public Speaking Competency Evaluation Form
(*Based on the work of the National Communication Association)

Speaker Name: _____

Date: _____

Type of Speech: _____

	Competency Levels Low/Moderate/High		
1: Chooses and narrows the topic appropriate for the audience and occasion.			
2: Communicates the thesis/specific clearly and in a manner appropriate to the audience and occasion.			
3: Provides supporting materials that are appropriate to the audience and occasion (e.g., statistics, examples, expert testimony).			
4: Clear and effective organizational pattern appropriate to the audience, occasion, and the topic.			
5: Uses language that is appropriate to the audience and occasion (clear, vivid, and imaginative).			
6: Uses vocal variety in rate, pitch, and volume used to heighten and maintain interest appropriate to the audience and occasion.			
7: Uses pronunciation, grammar, and articulation appropriate to the audience and occasion.			
8: Uses physical behaviors that support the verbal messages (gestures, eye contact, and use of proxemics).			

What I liked about this speech:

_____

_____

_____

_____

_____.

Public Speaking Competency Feedback and Development Form

**Highlighted items need more development

	Current level			
Organization and Content:	-	*OK*	+	++
Introduction · preview · attention getter · credibility · reason for listening				
Transitions · obvious · pause				
Organizational Pattern · clear · appropriate				
Central Idea · identifiable · focused				
Supporting Materials · smooth · names · authoritative				
Conclusion · signal end · summarize · repeat main points · closure · integrated				
Logistics · appropriate topic selection · appropriate length of speech · use of notes				
Delivery:				
Language · concrete · vivid · stories · avoid jargon				
Voice Quality · volume · rate · tone · flow				
Vocal Variety · inflection · pauses				
Kinesics · professional · energy · confident				
Eye Contact · scan · gaze · linger · inclusive				
Gestures · purposeful · integrated				
Utilization of Space · step up · step out				
Visual Aid(s):				
Design · clear · visible · professional				
Integration · smooth · purposeful				

The Civic Engagement Speech
Public Speaking Competency Evaluation Form
(*Based on the work of the National Communication Association)

Speaker Name: _____

Date: _____

Type of Speech: _____

Competency Levels
Low/Moderate/High

1: Chooses and narrows the topic appropriate for the audience and occasion.			
2: Communicates the thesis/specific clearly and in a manner appropriate to the audience and occasion.			
3: Provides supporting materials that are appropriate to the audience and occasion (e.g., statistics, examples, expert testimony).			
4: Clear and effective organizational pattern appropriate to the audience, occasion, and the topic.			
5: Uses language that is appropriate to the audience and occasion (clear, vivid, and imaginative).			
6: Uses vocal variety in rate, pitch, and volume used to heighten and maintain interest appropriate to the audience and occasion.			
7: Uses pronunciation, grammar, and articulation appropriate to the audience and occasion.			
8: Uses physical behaviors that support the verbal messages (gestures, eye contact, and use of proxemics).			

What I liked about this speech:

_____

_____

_____

_____

_____.

Name _____

Public Speaking Competency Feedback and Development Form

**Highlighted items need more development	Current level			
Organization and Content:	-	*OK*	+	++
Introduction · preview · attention getter · credibility · reason for listening				
Transitions · obvious · pause				
Organizational Pattern · clear · appropriate				
Central Idea · identifiable · focused				
Supporting Materials · smooth · names · authoritative				
Conclusion · signal end · summarize · repeat main points · closure · integrated				
Logistics · appropriate topic selection · appropriate length of speech · use of notes				
Delivery:				
Language · concrete · vivid · stories · avoid jargon				
Voice Quality · volume · rate · tone · flow				
Vocal Variety · inflection · pauses				
Kinesics · professional · energy · confident				
Eye Contact · scan · gaze · linger · inclusive				
Gestures · purposeful · integrated				
Utilization of Space · step up · step out				
Visual Aid(s):				
Design · clear · visible · professional				
Integration · smooth · purposeful				

The Civic Engagement Speech
Public Speaking Competency Evaluation Form

(*Based on the work of the National Communication Association)

Speaker Name: _____

Date: _____

Type of Speech: _____

Competency Levels
Low/Moderate/High

	Low	Moderate	High
1: Chooses and narrows the topic appropriate for the audience and occasion.			
2: Communicates the thesis/specific clearly and in a manner appropriate to the audience and occasion.			
3: Provides supporting materials that are appropriate to the audience and occasion (e.g., statistics, examples, expert testimony).			
4: Clear and effective organizational pattern appropriate to the audience, occasion, and the topic.			
5: Uses language that is appropriate to the audience and occasion (clear, vivid, and imaginative).			
6: Uses vocal variety in rate, pitch, and volume used to heighten and maintain interest appropriate to the audience and occasion.			
7: Uses pronunciation, grammar, and articulation appropriate to the audience and occasion.			
8: Uses physical behaviors that support the verbal messages (gestures, eye contact, and use of proxemics).			

What I liked about this speech:

_____

_____

_____

_____

_____.

Name _____

Public Speaking Competency Feedback and Development Form

**Highlighted items need more development

Highlighted items need more development	Current level			
Organization and Content:	-	*OK*	+	++
Introduction · preview · attention getter · credibility · reason for listening				
Transitions · obvious · pause				
Organizational Pattern · clear · appropriate				
Central Idea · identifiable · focused				
Supporting Materials · smooth · names · authoritative				
Conclusion · signal end · summarize · repeat main points · closure · integrated				
Logistics · appropriate topic selection · appropriate length of speech · use of notes				
Delivery:				
Language · concrete · vivid · stories · avoid jargon				
Voice Quality · volume · rate · tone · flow				
Vocal Variety · inflection · pauses				
Kinesics · professional · energy · confident				
Eye Contact · scan · gaze · linger · inclusive				
Gestures · purposeful · integrated				
Utilization of Space · step up · step out				
Visual Aid(s):				
Design · clear · visible · professional				
Integration · smooth · purposeful				

The Civic Engagement Speech
Public Speaking Competency Evaluation Form
(*Based on the work of the National Communication Association)

Speaker Name: _____

Date: _____

Type of Speech: _____

	Competency Levels _Low/Moderate/High_		
1: Chooses and narrows the topic appropriate for the audience and occasion.			
2: Communicates the thesis/specific clearly and in a manner appropriate to the audience and occasion.			
3: Provides supporting materials that are appropriate to the audience and occasion (e.g., statistics, examples, expert testimony).			
4: Clear and effective organizational pattern appropriate to the audience, occasion, and the topic.			
5: Uses language that is appropriate to the audience and occasion (clear, vivid, and imaginative).			
6: Uses vocal variety in rate, pitch, and volume used to heighten and maintain interest appropriate to the audience and occasion.			
7: Uses pronunciation, grammar, and articulation appropriate to the audience and occasion.			
8: Uses physical behaviors that support the verbal messages (gestures, eye contact, and use of proxemics).			

What I liked about this speech:

_____

_____

_____

_____

_____.

Name _____

Public Speaking Competency Feedback and Development Form

**Highlighted items need more development

		Current level		
Organization and Content:	-	*OK*	+	++
Introduction · preview · attention getter · credibility · reason for listening				
Transitions · obvious · pause				
Organizational Pattern · clear · appropriate				
Central Idea · identifiable · focused				
Supporting Materials · smooth · names · authoritative				
Conclusion · signal end · summarize · repeat main points · closure · integrated				
Logistics · appropriate topic selection · appropriate length of speech · use of notes				
Delivery:				
Language · concrete · vivid · stories · avoid jargon				
Voice Quality · volume · rate · tone · flow				
Vocal Variety · inflection · pauses				
Kinesics · professional · energy · confident				
Eye Contact · scan · gaze · linger · inclusive				
Gestures · purposeful · integrated				
Utilization of Space · step up · step out				
Visual Aid(s):				
Design · clear · visible · professional				
Integration · smooth · purposeful				

The Civic Engagement Speech
Public Speaking Competency Evaluation Form
(*Based on the work of the National Communication Association)

Speaker Name: _____

Date: _____

Type of Speech: _____

Competency Levels
Low/Moderate/High

	Low	Moderate	High
1: Chooses and narrows the topic appropriate for the audience and occasion.			
2: Communicates the thesis/specific clearly and in a manner appropriate to the audience and occasion.			
3: Provides supporting materials that are appropriate to the audience and occasion (e.g., statistics, examples, expert testimony).			
4: Clear and effective organizational pattern appropriate to the audience, occasion, and the topic.			
5: Uses language that is appropriate to the audience and occasion (clear, vivid, and imaginative).			
6: Uses vocal variety in rate, pitch, and volume used to heighten and maintain interest appropriate to the audience and occasion.			
7: Uses pronunciation, grammar, and articulation appropriate to the audience and occasion.			
8: Uses physical behaviors that support the verbal messages (gestures, eye contact, and use of proxemics).			

What I liked about this speech:

_____

_____

_____

_____

_____.

Name _____

Public Speaking Competency Feedback and Development Form

**Highlighted items need more development

	Current level			
Organization and Content:	-	*OK*	+	++
Introduction · preview · attention getter · credibility · reason for listening				
Transitions · obvious · pause				
Organizational Pattern · clear · appropriate				
Central Idea · identifiable · focused				
Supporting Materials · smooth · names · authoritative				
Conclusion · signal end · summarize · repeat main points · closure · integrated				
Logistics · appropriate topic selection · appropriate length of speech · use of notes				
Delivery:				
Language · concrete · vivid · stories · avoid jargon				
Voice Quality · volume · rate · tone · flow				
Vocal Variety · inflection · pauses				
Kinesics · professional · energy · confident				
Eye Contact · scan · gaze · linger · inclusive				
Gestures · purposeful · integrated				
Utilization of Space · step up · step out				
Visual Aid(s):				
Design · clear · visible · professional				
Integration · smooth · purposeful				

The Civic Engagement Speech
Public Speaking Competency Evaluation Form
(*Based on the work of the National Communication Association)

Speaker Name: _____

Date: _____

Type of Speech: _____

Competency Levels
Low/Moderate/High

	Low	Moderate	High
1: Chooses and narrows the topic appropriate for the audience and occasion.			
2: Communicates the thesis/specific clearly and in a manner appropriate to the audience and occasion.			
3: Provides supporting materials that are appropriate to the audience and occasion (e.g., statistics, examples, expert testimony).			
4: Clear and effective organizational pattern appropriate to the audience, occasion, and the topic.			
5: Uses language that is appropriate to the audience and occasion (clear, vivid, and imaginative).			
6: Uses vocal variety in rate, pitch, and volume used to heighten and maintain interest appropriate to the audience and occasion.			
7: Uses pronunciation, grammar, and articulation appropriate to the audience and occasion.			
8: Uses physical behaviors that support the verbal messages (gestures, eye contact, and use of proxemics).			

What I liked about this speech:

_____

_____

_____

_____

_____.

Public Speaking Competency Feedback and Development Form

**Highlighted items need more development

	Current level			
Organization and Content:	-	*OK*	+	++
Introduction · preview · attention getter · credibility · reason for listening				
Transitions · obvious · pause				
Organizational Pattern · clear · appropriate				
Central Idea · identifiable · focused				
Supporting Materials · smooth · names · authoritative				
Conclusion · signal end · summarize · repeat main points · closure · integrated				
Logistics · appropriate topic selection · appropriate length of speech · use of notes				
Delivery:				
Language · concrete · vivid · stories · avoid jargon				
Voice Quality · volume · rate · tone · flow				
Vocal Variety · inflection · pauses				
Kinesics · professional · energy · confident				
Eye Contact · scan · gaze · linger · inclusive				
Gestures · purposeful · integrated				
Utilization of Space · step up · step out				
Visual Aid(s):				
Design · clear · visible · professional				
Integration · smooth · purposeful				

The Civic Engagement Speech
Public Speaking Competency Evaluation Form
(*Based on the work of the National Communication Association)

Speaker Name: _____

Date: _____

Type of Speech: _____

Competency Levels
Low/Moderate/High

1: Chooses and narrows the topic appropriate for the audience and occasion.			
2: Communicates the thesis/specific clearly and in a manner appropriate to the audience and occasion.			
3: Provides supporting materials that are appropriate to the audience and occasion (e.g., statistics, examples, expert testimony).			
4: Clear and effective organizational pattern appropriate to the audience, occasion, and the topic.			
5: Uses language that is appropriate to the audience and occasion (clear, vivid, and imaginative).			
6: Uses vocal variety in rate, pitch, and volume used to heighten and maintain interest appropriate to the audience and occasion.			
7: Uses pronunciation, grammar, and articulation appropriate to the audience and occasion.			
8: Uses physical behaviors that support the verbal messages (gestures, eye contact, and use of proxemics).			

What I liked about this speech:

_____

_____

_____

_____

_____.

Name _____

Public Speaking Competency Feedback and Development Form

**Highlighted items need more development

**Highlighted items need more development	Current level			
Organization and Content:	-	*OK*	+	++
Introduction · preview · attention getter · credibility · reason for listening				
Transitions · obvious · pause				
Organizational Pattern · clear · appropriate				
Central Idea · identifiable · focused				
Supporting Materials · smooth · names · authoritative				
Conclusion · signal end · summarize · repeat main points · closure · integrated				
Logistics · appropriate topic selection · appropriate length of speech · use of notes				
Delivery:				
Language · concrete · vivid · stories · avoid jargon				
Voice Quality · volume · rate · tone · flow				
Vocal Variety · inflection · pauses				
Kinesics · professional · energy · confident				
Eye Contact · scan · gaze · linger · inclusive				
Gestures · purposeful · integrated				
Utilization of Space · step up · step out				
Visual Aid(s):				
Design · clear · visible · professional				
Integration · smooth · purposeful				

The Civic Engagement Speech
Public Speaking Competency Evaluation Form
(*Based on the work of the National Communication Association)

Speaker Name: _____

Date: _____

Type of Speech: _____

Competency Levels
Low/Moderate/High

	Low	Moderate	High
1: Chooses and narrows the topic appropriate for the audience and occasion.			
2: Communicates the thesis/specific clearly and in a manner appropriate to the audience and occasion.			
3: Provides supporting materials that are appropriate to the audience and occasion (e.g., statistics, examples, expert testimony).			
4: Clear and effective organizational pattern appropriate to the audience, occasion, and the topic.			
5: Uses language that is appropriate to the audience and occasion (clear, vivid, and imaginative).			
6: Uses vocal variety in rate, pitch, and volume used to heighten and maintain interest appropriate to the audience and occasion.			
7: Uses pronunciation, grammar, and articulation appropriate to the audience and occasion.			
8: Uses physical behaviors that support the verbal messages (gestures, eye contact, and use of proxemics).			

What I liked about this speech:

_____

_____

_____

_____

_____.

Public Speaking Competency Feedback and Development Form

**Highlighted items need more development

	Current level			
Organization and Content:	-	*OK*	+	++
Introduction · preview · attention getter · credibility · reason for listening				
Transitions · obvious · pause				
Organizational Pattern · clear · appropriate				
Central Idea · identifiable · focused				
Supporting Materials · smooth · names · authoritative				
Conclusion · signal end · summarize · repeat main points · closure · integrated				
Logistics · appropriate topic selection · appropriate length of speech · use of notes				
Delivery:				
Language · concrete · vivid · stories · avoid jargon				
Voice Quality · volume · rate · tone · flow				
Vocal Variety · inflection · pauses				
Kinesics · professional · energy · confident				
Eye Contact · scan · gaze · linger · inclusive				
Gestures · purposeful · integrated				
Utilization of Space · step up · step out				
Visual Aid(s):				
Design · clear · visible · professional				
Integration · smooth · purposeful				

The Ceremonial Speech
Public Speaking Competency Evaluation Form
(*Based on the work of the National Communication Association)

Speaker Name: _____

Date: _____

Type of Speech: _____

Competency Levels
Low/Moderate/High

	Low	Moderate	High
1: Chooses and narrows the topic appropriate for the audience and occasion.			
2: Communicates the thesis/specific clearly and in a manner appropriate to the audience and occasion.			
3: Provides supporting materials that are appropriate to the audience and occasion (e.g., statistics, examples, expert testimony).			
4: Clear and effective organizational pattern appropriate to the audience, occasion, and the topic.			
5: Uses language that is appropriate to the audience and occasion (clear, vivid, and imaginative).			
6: Uses vocal variety in rate, pitch, and volume used to heighten and maintain interest appropriate to the audience and occasion.			
7: Uses pronunciation, grammar, and articulation appropriate to the audience and occasion.			
8: Uses physical behaviors that support the verbal messages (gestures, eye contact, and use of proxemics).			

What I liked about this speech:

_____

_____

_____

_____

_____.

Name _____

Public Speaking Competency Feedback and Development Form

**Highlighted items need more development

	Current level			
Organization and Content:	-	*OK*	+	++
Introduction · preview · attention getter · credibility · reason for listening				
Transitions · obvious · pause				
Organizational Pattern · clear · appropriate				
Central Idea · identifiable · focused				
Supporting Materials · smooth · names · authoritative				
Conclusion · signal end · summarize · repeat main points · closure · integrated				
Logistics · appropriate topic selection · appropriate length of speech · use of notes				
Delivery:				
Language · concrete · vivid · stories · avoid jargon				
Voice Quality · volume · rate · tone · flow				
Vocal Variety · inflection · pauses				
Kinesics · professional · energy · confident				
Eye Contact · scan · gaze · linger · inclusive				
Gestures · purposeful · integrated				
Utilization of Space · step up · step out				
Visual Aid(s):				
Design · clear · visible · professional				
Integration · smooth · purposeful				

The Ceremonial Speech
Public Speaking Competency Evaluation Form
(*Based on the work of the National Communication Association)

Speaker Name: _____

Date: _____

Type of Speech: _____

<table>
<tr><td></td><td colspan="3">Competency Levels
Low/Moderate/High</td></tr>
<tr><td>1: Chooses and narrows the topic appropriate for the audience and occasion.</td><td></td><td></td><td></td></tr>
<tr><td>2: Communicates the thesis/specific clearly and in a manner appropriate to the audience and occasion.</td><td></td><td></td><td></td></tr>
<tr><td>3: Provides supporting materials that are appropriate to the audience and occasion (e.g., statistics, examples, expert testimony).</td><td></td><td></td><td></td></tr>
<tr><td>4: Clear and effective organizational pattern appropriate to the audience, occasion, and the topic.</td><td></td><td></td><td></td></tr>
<tr><td>5: Uses language that is appropriate to the audience and occasion (clear, vivid, and imaginative).</td><td></td><td></td><td></td></tr>
<tr><td>6: Uses vocal variety in rate, pitch, and volume used to heighten and maintain interest appropriate to the audience and occasion.</td><td></td><td></td><td></td></tr>
<tr><td>7: Uses pronunciation, grammar, and articulation appropriate to the audience and occasion.</td><td></td><td></td><td></td></tr>
<tr><td>8: Uses physical behaviors that support the verbal messages (gestures, eye contact, and use of proxemics).</td><td></td><td></td><td></td></tr>
</table>

What I liked about this speech:

_____

_____

_____

_____

_____ .

Public Speaking Competency Feedback and Development Form

**Highlighted items need more development

**Highlighted items need more development	Current level			
Organization and Content:	-	*OK*	+	++
Introduction · preview · attention getter · credibility · reason for listening				
Transitions · obvious · pause				
Organizational Pattern · clear · appropriate				
Central Idea · identifiable · focused				
Supporting Materials · smooth · names · authoritative				
Conclusion · signal end · summarize · repeat main points · closure · integrated				
Logistics · appropriate topic selection · appropriate length of speech · use of notes				
Delivery:				
Language · concrete · vivid · stories · avoid jargon				
Voice Quality · volume · rate · tone · flow				
Vocal Variety · inflection · pauses				
Kinesics · professional · energy · confident				
Eye Contact · scan · gaze · linger · inclusive				
Gestures · purposeful · integrated				
Utilization of Space · step up · step out				
Visual Aid(s):				
Design · clear · visible · professional				
Integration · smooth · purposeful				

The Ceremonial Speech
Public Speaking Competency Evaluation Form
(*Based on the work of the National Communication Association)

Speaker Name: _____

Date: _____

Type of Speech: _____

Competency Levels
Low/Moderate/High

	Low	Moderate	High
1: Chooses and narrows the topic appropriate for the audience and occasion.			
2: Communicates the thesis/specific clearly and in a manner appropriate to the audience and occasion.			
3: Provides supporting materials that are appropriate to the audience and occasion (e.g., statistics, examples, expert testimony).			
4: Clear and effective organizational pattern appropriate to the audience, occasion, and the topic.			
5: Uses language that is appropriate to the audience and occasion (clear, vivid, and imaginative).			
6: Uses vocal variety in rate, pitch, and volume used to heighten and maintain interest appropriate to the audience and occasion.			
7: Uses pronunciation, grammar, and articulation appropriate to the audience and occasion.			
8: Uses physical behaviors that support the verbal messages (gestures, eye contact, and use of proxemics).			

What I liked about this speech:

_____

_____

_____

_____

_____.

Name _____

Public Speaking Competency Feedback and Development Form

**Highlighted items need more development   Current level

Organization and Content:	-	*OK*	+	++
Introduction · preview · attention getter · credibility · reason for listening				
Transitions · obvious · pause				
Organizational Pattern · clear · appropriate				
Central Idea · identifiable · focused				
Supporting Materials · smooth · names · authoritative				
Conclusion · signal end · summarize · repeat main points · closure · integrated				
Logistics · appropriate topic selection · appropriate length of speech · use of notes				
Delivery:				
Language · concrete · vivid · stories · avoid jargon				
Voice Quality · volume · rate · tone · flow				
Vocal Variety · inflection · pauses				
Kinesics · professional · energy · confident				
Eye Contact · scan · gaze · linger · inclusive				
Gestures · purposeful · integrated				
Utilization of Space · step up · step out				
Visual Aid(s):				
Design · clear · visible · professional				
Integration · smooth · purposeful				

The Ceremonial Speech
Public Speaking Competency Evaluation Form
(*Based on the work of the National Communication Association)

Speaker Name: _____

Date: _____

Type of Speech: _____

Competency Levels
Low/Moderate/High

1: Chooses and narrows the topic appropriate for the audience and occasion.			
2: Communicates the thesis/specific clearly and in a manner appropriate to the audience and occasion.			
3: Provides supporting materials that are appropriate to the audience and occasion (e.g., statistics, examples, expert testimony).			
4: Clear and effective organizational pattern appropriate to the audience, occasion, and the topic.			
5: Uses language that is appropriate to the audience and occasion (clear, vivid, and imaginative).			
6: Uses vocal variety in rate, pitch, and volume used to heighten and maintain interest appropriate to the audience and occasion.			
7: Uses pronunciation, grammar, and articulation appropriate to the audience and occasion.			
8: Uses physical behaviors that support the verbal messages (gestures, eye contact, and use of proxemics).			

What I liked about this speech:

_____

_____

_____

_____

_____.

Name _____

Public Speaking Competency Feedback and Development Form

**Highlighted items need more development

	Current level			
Organization and Content:	-	*OK*	+	++
Introduction · preview · attention getter · credibility · reason for listening				
Transitions · obvious · pause				
Organizational Pattern · clear · appropriate				
Central Idea · identifiable · focused				
Supporting Materials · smooth · names · authoritative				
Conclusion · signal end · summarize · repeat main points · closure · integrated				
Logistics · appropriate topic selection · appropriate length of speech · use of notes				
Delivery:				
Language · concrete · vivid · stories · avoid jargon				
Voice Quality · volume · rate · tone · flow				
Vocal Variety · inflection · pauses				
Kinesics · professional · energy · confident				
Eye Contact · scan · gaze · linger · inclusive				
Gestures · purposeful · integrated				
Utilization of Space · step up · step out				
Visual Aid(s):				
Design · clear · visible · professional				
Integration · smooth · purposeful				

The Ceremonial Speech
Public Speaking Competency Evaluation Form
(*Based on the work of the National Communication Association)

Speaker Name: _____

Date: _____

Type of Speech: _____

Competency Levels
Low/Moderate/High

1: Chooses and narrows the topic appropriate for the audience and occasion.			
2: Communicates the thesis/specific clearly and in a manner appropriate to the audience and occasion.			
3: Provides supporting materials that are appropriate to the audience and occasion (e.g., statistics, examples, expert testimony).			
4: Clear and effective organizational pattern appropriate to the audience, occasion, and the topic.			
5: Uses language that is appropriate to the audience and occasion (clear, vivid, and imaginative).			
6: Uses vocal variety in rate, pitch, and volume used to heighten and maintain interest appropriate to the audience and occasion.			
7: Uses pronunciation, grammar, and articulation appropriate to the audience and occasion.			
8: Uses physical behaviors that support the verbal messages (gestures, eye contact, and use of proxemics).			

What I liked about this speech:

_____

_____

_____

_____

_____.

Name _____

Public Speaking Competency Feedback and Development Form

**Highlighted items need more development		Current level		
Organization and Content:	-	*OK*	+	++
Introduction · preview · attention getter · credibility · reason for listening				
Transitions · obvious · pause				
Organizational Pattern · clear · appropriate				
Central Idea · identifiable · focused				
Supporting Materials · smooth · names · authoritative				
Conclusion · signal end · summarize · repeat main points · closure · integrated				
Logistics · appropriate topic selection · appropriate length of speech · use of notes				
Delivery:				
Language · concrete · vivid · stories · avoid jargon				
Voice Quality · volume · rate · tone · flow				
Vocal Variety · inflection · pauses				
Kinesics · professional · energy · confident				
Eye Contact · scan · gaze · linger · inclusive				
Gestures · purposeful · integrated				
Utilization of Space · step up · step out				
Visual Aid(s):				
Design · clear · visible · professional				
Integration · smooth · purposeful				

The Ceremonial Speech
Public Speaking Competency Evaluation Form
(*Based on the work of the National Communication Association)

Speaker Name: _____

Date: _____

Type of Speech: _____

Competency Levels
Low/Moderate/High

1: Chooses and narrows the topic appropriate for the audience and occasion.			
2: Communicates the thesis/specific clearly and in a manner appropriate to the audience and occasion.			
3: Provides supporting materials that are appropriate to the audience and occasion (e.g., statistics, examples, expert testimony).			
4: Clear and effective organizational pattern appropriate to the audience, occasion, and the topic.			
5: Uses language that is appropriate to the audience and occasion (clear, vivid, and imaginative).			
6: Uses vocal variety in rate, pitch, and volume used to heighten and maintain interest appropriate to the audience and occasion.			
7: Uses pronunciation, grammar, and articulation appropriate to the audience and occasion.			
8: Uses physical behaviors that support the verbal messages (gestures, eye contact, and use of proxemics).			

What I liked about this speech:

_____

_____

_____

_____

_____.

Name _____

Public Speaking Competency Feedback and Development Form

**Highlighted items need more development

**Highlighted items need more development	Current level			
Organization and Content:	-	*OK*	+	++
Introduction · preview · attention getter · credibility · reason for listening				
Transitions · obvious · pause				
Organizational Pattern · clear · appropriate				
Central Idea · identifiable · focused				
Supporting Materials · smooth · names · authoritative				
Conclusion · signal end · summarize · repeat main points · closure · integrated				
Logistics · appropriate topic selection · appropriate length of speech · use of notes				
Delivery:				
Language · concrete · vivid · stories · avoid jargon				
Voice Quality · volume · rate · tone · flow				
Vocal Variety · inflection · pauses				
Kinesics · professional · energy · confident				
Eye Contact · scan · gaze · linger · inclusive				
Gestures · purposeful · integrated				
Utilization of Space · step up · step out				
Visual Aid(s):				
Design · clear · visible · professional				
Integration · smooth · purposeful				

The Ceremonial Speech
Public Speaking Competency Evaluation Form
(*Based on the work of the National Communication Association)

Speaker Name: _____

Date: _____

Type of Speech: _____

	Competency Levels Low/Moderate/High		
1: Chooses and narrows the topic appropriate for the audience and occasion.			
2: Communicates the thesis/specific clearly and in a manner appropriate to the audience and occasion.			
3: Provides supporting materials that are appropriate to the audience and occasion (e.g., statistics, examples, expert testimony).			
4: Clear and effective organizational pattern appropriate to the audience, occasion, and the topic.			
5: Uses language that is appropriate to the audience and occasion (clear, vivid, and imaginative).			
6: Uses vocal variety in rate, pitch, and volume used to heighten and maintain interest appropriate to the audience and occasion.			
7: Uses pronunciation, grammar, and articulation appropriate to the audience and occasion.			
8: Uses physical behaviors that support the verbal messages (gestures, eye contact, and use of proxemics).			

What I liked about this speech:

_____

_____

_____

_____

_____.

97

Name ____________________

Public Speaking Competency Feedback and Development Form

**Highlighted items need more development — Current level

Organization and Content:	-	*OK*	+	++
Introduction · preview · attention getter · credibility · reason for listening				
Transitions · obvious · pause				
Organizational Pattern · clear · appropriate				
Central Idea · identifiable · focused				
Supporting Materials · smooth · names · authoritative				
Conclusion · signal end · summarize · repeat main points · closure · integrated				
Logistics · appropriate topic selection · appropriate length of speech · use of notes				
Delivery:				
Language · concrete · vivid · stories · avoid jargon				
Voice Quality · volume · rate · tone · flow				
Vocal Variety · inflection · pauses				
Kinesics · professional · energy · confident				
Eye Contact · scan · gaze · linger · inclusive				
Gestures · purposeful · integrated				
Utilization of Space · step up · step out				
Visual Aid(s):				
Design · clear · visible · professional				
Integration · smooth · purposeful				

The Ceremonial Speech
Public Speaking Competency Evaluation Form
(*Based on the work of the National Communication Association)

Speaker Name: _____

Date: _____

Type of Speech: _____

	Competency Levels Low/Moderate/High		
1: Chooses and narrows the topic appropriate for the audience and occasion.			
2: Communicates the thesis/specific clearly and in a manner appropriate to the audience and occasion.			
3: Provides supporting materials that are appropriate to the audience and occasion (e.g., statistics, examples, expert testimony).			
4: Clear and effective organizational pattern appropriate to the audience, occasion, and the topic.			
5: Uses language that is appropriate to the audience and occasion (clear, vivid, and imaginative).			
6: Uses vocal variety in rate, pitch, and volume used to heighten and maintain interest appropriate to the audience and occasion.			
7: Uses pronunciation, grammar, and articulation appropriate to the audience and occasion.			
8: Uses physical behaviors that support the verbal messages (gestures, eye contact, and use of proxemics).			

What I liked about this speech:

_____

_____

_____

_____

_____.

Name _____

Public Speaking Competency Feedback and Development Form

**Highlighted items need more development   Current level

Organization and Content:	-	OK	+	++
Introduction · preview · attention getter · credibility · reason for listening				
Transitions · obvious · pause				
Organizational Pattern · clear · appropriate				
Central Idea · identifiable · focused				
Supporting Materials · smooth · names · authoritative				
Conclusion · signal end · summarize · repeat main points · closure · integrated				
Logistics · appropriate topic selection · appropriate length of speech · use of notes				
Delivery:				
Language · concrete · vivid · stories · avoid jargon				
Voice Quality · volume · rate · tone · flow				
Vocal Variety · inflection · pauses				
Kinesics · professional · energy · confident				
Eye Contact · scan · gaze · linger · inclusive				
Gestures · purposeful · integrated				
Utilization of Space · step up · step out				
Visual Aid(s):				
Design · clear · visible · professional				
Integration · smooth · purposeful				

The Ceremonial Speech
Public Speaking Competency Evaluation Form
(*Based on the work of the National Communication Association)

Speaker Name: _____

Date: _____

Type of Speech: _____

Competency Levels
Low/Moderate/High

1: Chooses and narrows the topic appropriate for the audience and occasion.			
2: Communicates the thesis/specific clearly and in a manner appropriate to the audience and occasion.			
3: Provides supporting materials that are appropriate to the audience and occasion (e.g., statistics, examples, expert testimony).			
4: Clear and effective organizational pattern appropriate to the audience, occasion, and the topic.			
5: Uses language that is appropriate to the audience and occasion (clear, vivid, and imaginative).			
6: Uses vocal variety in rate, pitch, and volume used to heighten and maintain interest appropriate to the audience and occasion.			
7: Uses pronunciation, grammar, and articulation appropriate to the audience and occasion.			
8: Uses physical behaviors that support the verbal messages (gestures, eye contact, and use of proxemics).			

What I liked about this speech:

_____
_____
_____
_____
_____.

101

Public Speaking Competency Feedback and Development Form

**Highlighted items need more development   Current level

Organization and Content:	-	*OK*	+	++
Introduction · preview · attention getter · credibility · reason for listening				
Transitions · obvious · pause				
Organizational Pattern · clear · appropriate				
Central Idea · identifiable · focused				
Supporting Materials · smooth · names · authoritative				
Conclusion · signal end · summarize · repeat main points · closure · integrated				
Logistics · appropriate topic selection · appropriate length of speech · use of notes				
Delivery:				
Language · concrete · vivid · stories · avoid jargon				
Voice Quality · volume · rate · tone · flow				
Vocal Variety · inflection · pauses				
Kinesics · professional · energy · confident				
Eye Contact · scan · gaze · linger · inclusive				
Gestures · purposeful · integrated				
Utilization of Space · step up · step out				
Visual Aid(s):				
Design · clear · visible · professional				
Integration · smooth · purposeful				

The Ceremonial Speech
Public Speaking Competency Evaluation Form
(*Based on the work of the National Communication Association)

Speaker Name: _____

Date: _____

Type of Speech: _____

Competency Levels
Low/Moderate/High

	Low	Moderate	High
1: Chooses and narrows the topic appropriate for the audience and occasion.			
2: Communicates the thesis/specific clearly and in a manner appropriate to the audience and occasion.			
3: Provides supporting materials that are appropriate to the audience and occasion (e.g., statistics, examples, expert testimony).			
4: Clear and effective organizational pattern appropriate to the audience, occasion, and the topic.			
5: Uses language that is appropriate to the audience and occasion (clear, vivid, and imaginative).			
6: Uses vocal variety in rate, pitch, and volume used to heighten and maintain interest appropriate to the audience and occasion.			
7: Uses pronunciation, grammar, and articulation appropriate to the audience and occasion.			
8: Uses physical behaviors that support the verbal messages (gestures, eye contact, and use of proxemics).			

What I liked about this speech:

_____

_____

_____

_____

_____.

Name _____

Public Speaking Competency Feedback and Development Form

**Highlighted items need more development

	Current level			
Organization and Content:	-	*OK*	+	++
Introduction · preview · attention getter · credibility · reason for listening				
Transitions · obvious · pause				
Organizational Pattern · clear · appropriate				
Central Idea · identifiable · focused				
Supporting Materials · smooth · names · authoritative				
Conclusion · signal end · summarize · repeat main points · closure · integrated				
Logistics · appropriate topic selection · appropriate length of speech · use of notes				
Delivery:				
Language · concrete · vivid · stories · avoid jargon				
Voice Quality · volume · rate · tone · flow				
Vocal Variety · inflection · pauses				
Kinesics · professional · energy · confident				
Eye Contact · scan · gaze · linger · inclusive				
Gestures · purposeful · integrated				
Utilization of Space · step up · step out				
Visual Aid(s):				
Design · clear · visible · professional				
Integration · smooth · purposeful				

Impromptu Speech

(From the Competent Speaker Form adopted from the National Communication Association)

Name_____   Date_____

PRESENTATIONAL COMPETENCIES

<u>Competency Levels</u>
Low / Moderate / High

Competency One: **Uses an effective attention-getter.**

_____ _____ _____

Competency Two: **Uses language appropriately.**

_____ _____ _____

Competency Three: **Uses vocal variety in rate, pitch, & intensity.**

_____ _____ _____

Competency Four: **Avoids long (unintended) pauses in Speech Presentation.**

_____ _____ _____

Competency Five: **Uses physical behaviors (gestures) that support the verbal message.**

_____ _____ _____

Time: _____

Comments/Suggestions for speaker improvement:
(Also see Sprague text p. 168 – "Speaking Impromptu")

_____

_____

_____

_____

_____

_____

Name ____________________

Public Speaking Competency Feedback and Development Form

**Highlighted items need more development   Current level

Organization and Content:	-	*OK*	+	++
Introduction · preview · attention getter · credibility · reason for listening				
Transitions · obvious · pause				
Organizational Pattern · clear · appropriate				
Central Idea · identifiable · focused				
Supporting Materials · smooth · names · authoritative				
Conclusion · signal end · summarize · repeat main points · closure · integrated				
Logistics · appropriate topic selection · appropriate length of speech · use of notes				
Delivery:				
Language · concrete · vivid · stories · avoid jargon				
Voice Quality · volume · rate · tone · flow				
Vocal Variety · inflection · pauses				
Kinesics · professional · energy · confident				
Eye Contact · scan · gaze · linger · inclusive				
Gestures · purposeful · integrated				
Utilization of Space · step up · step out				
Visual Aid(s):				
Design · clear · visible · professional				
Integration · smooth · purposeful				

Impromptu Speech

(From the Competent Speaker Form adopted from the National Communication Association)

Name_____   Date_____

PRESENTATIONAL COMPETENCIES

<u>Competency Levels</u>
Low / Moderate / High

Competency One: **Uses an effective attention-getter.**

_____ _____ _____

Competency Two: **Uses language appropriately.**

_____ _____ _____

Competency Three: **Uses vocal variety in rate, pitch, & intensity.**

_____ _____ _____

Competency Four: **Avoids long (unintended) pauses in Speech Presentation.**

_____ _____ _____

Competency Five: **Uses physical behaviors (gestures) that support the verbal message.**

_____ _____ _____

Time: _____

Comments/Suggestions for speaker improvement:
  (Also see Sprague text p. 168 – "Speaking Impromptu")

_____
_____
_____
_____
_____
_____

Name _____

Public Speaking Competency Feedback and Development Form

**Highlighted items need more development

		Current level		
Organization and Content:	-	*OK*	+	++
Introduction · preview · attention getter · credibility · reason for listening				
Transitions · obvious · pause				
Organizational Pattern · clear · appropriate				
Central Idea · identifiable · focused				
Supporting Materials · smooth · names · authoritative				
Conclusion · signal end · summarize · repeat main points · closure · integrated				
Logistics · appropriate topic selection · appropriate length of speech · use of notes				
Delivery:				
Language · concrete · vivid · stories · avoid jargon				
Voice Quality · volume · rate · tone · flow				
Vocal Variety · inflection · pauses				
Kinesics · professional · energy · confident				
Eye Contact · scan · gaze · linger · inclusive				
Gestures · purposeful · integrated				
Utilization of Space · step up · step out				
Visual Aid(s):				
Design · clear · visible · professional				
Integration · smooth · purposeful				

Impromptu Speech

(From the Competent Speaker Form adopted from the National Communication Association)

Name_____   Date_____

PRESENTATIONAL COMPETENCIES

Competency One: **Uses an effective attention-getter.**

_____ _____ _____

Competency Two: **Uses language appropriately.**

_____ _____ _____

Competency Three: **Uses vocal variety in rate, pitch, & intensity.**

_____ _____ _____

Competency Four: **Avoids long (unintended) pauses in Speech Presentation.**

_____ _____ _____

Competency Five: **Uses physical behaviors (gestures) that support the verbal message.**

_____ _____ _____

Time: _____

Comments/Suggestions for speaker improvement:

(Also see Sprague text p. 168 – "Speaking Impromptu")

_____

_____

_____

_____

_____

_____

Name _____

Public Speaking Competency Feedback and Development Form

**Highlighted items need more development

**Highlighted items need more development	Current level			
Organization and Content:	-	*OK*	+	++
Introduction · preview · attention getter · credibility · reason for listening				
Transitions · obvious · pause				
Organizational Pattern · clear · appropriate				
Central Idea · identifiable · focused				
Supporting Materials · smooth · names · authoritative				
Conclusion · signal end · summarize · repeat main points · closure · integrated				
Logistics · appropriate topic selection · appropriate length of speech · use of notes				
Delivery:				
Language · concrete · vivid · stories · avoid jargon				
Voice Quality · volume · rate · tone · flow				
Vocal Variety · inflection · pauses				
Kinesics · professional · energy · confident				
Eye Contact · scan · gaze · linger · inclusive				
Gestures · purposeful · integrated				
Utilization of Space · step up · step out				
Visual Aid(s):				
Design · clear · visible · professional				
Integration · smooth · purposeful				

Impromptu Speech

(From the Competent Speaker Form adopted from the National Communication Association)

Name_____   Date_____

PRESENTATIONAL COMPETENCIES

<u>Competency Levels</u>
Low / Moderate / High

Competency One: **Uses an effective attention-getter.**

_____ _____ _____

Competency Two: **Uses language appropriately**.

_____ _____ _____

Competency Three: **Uses vocal variety in rate, pitch, & intensity.**

_____ _____ _____

Competency Four: **Avoids long (unintended) pauses in Speech Presentation.**

_____ _____ _____

Competency Five: **Uses physical behaviors (gestures) that support the verbal message.**

_____ _____ _____

Time: _____

Comments/Suggestions for speaker improvement:
(Also see Sprague text p. 168 – "Speaking Impromptu")

_____

_____

_____

_____

_____

_____

Name _____

Public Speaking Competency Feedback and Development Form

**Highlighted items need more development

	Current level			
Organization and Content:	-	*OK*	+	++
Introduction · preview · attention getter · credibility · reason for listening				
Transitions · obvious · pause				
Organizational Pattern · clear · appropriate				
Central Idea · identifiable · focused				
Supporting Materials · smooth · names · authoritative				
Conclusion · signal end · summarize · repeat main points · closure · integrated				
Logistics · appropriate topic selection · appropriate length of speech · use of notes				
Delivery:				
Language · concrete · vivid · stories · avoid jargon				
Voice Quality · volume · rate · tone · flow				
Vocal Variety · inflection · pauses				
Kinesics · professional · energy · confident				
Eye Contact · scan · gaze · linger · inclusive				
Gestures · purposeful · integrated				
Utilization of Space · step up · step out				
Visual Aid(s):				
Design · clear · visible · professional				
Integration · smooth · purposeful				

Impromptu Speech

(From the Competent Speaker Form adopted from the National Communication Association)

Name_____   Date_____

PRESENTATIONAL COMPETENCIES

<u>Competency Levels</u>
Low / Moderate / High

Competency One: **Uses an effective attention-getter.**

_____ _____ _____

Competency Two: **Uses language appropriately**.

_____ _____ _____

Competency Three: **Uses vocal variety in rate, pitch, & intensity.**

_____ _____ _____

Competency Four: **Avoids long (unintended) pauses in Speech Presentation.**

_____ _____ _____

Competency Five: **Uses physical behaviors (gestures) that support the verbal message.**

_____ _____ _____

Time: _____

Comments/Suggestions for speaker improvement:

(Also see Sprague text p. 168 – "Speaking Impromptu")

_____

_____

_____

_____

_____

_____

Public Speaking Competency Feedback and Development Form

**Highlighted items need more development

**Highlighted items need more development	Current level			
Organization and Content:	-	*OK*	+	++
Introduction · preview · attention getter · credibility · reason for listening				
Transitions · obvious · pause				
Organizational Pattern · clear · appropriate				
Central Idea · identifiable · focused				
Supporting Materials · smooth · names · authoritative				
Conclusion · signal end · summarize · repeat main points · closure · integrated				
Logistics · appropriate topic selection · appropriate length of speech · use of notes				
Delivery:				
Language · concrete · vivid · stories · avoid jargon				
Voice Quality · volume · rate · tone · flow				
Vocal Variety · inflection · pauses				
Kinesics · professional · energy · confident				
Eye Contact · scan · gaze · linger · inclusive				
Gestures · purposeful · integrated				
Utilization of Space · step up · step out				
Visual Aid(s):				
Design · clear · visible · professional				
Integration · smooth · purposeful				

Impromptu Speech

(From the Competent Speaker Form adopted from the National Communication Association)

Name_____   Date_____

PRESENTATIONAL COMPETENCIES

<u>Competency Levels</u>
Low / Moderate / High

Competency One: **Uses an effective attention-getter.**

_____ _____ _____

Competency Two: **Uses language appropriately.**

_____ _____ _____

Competency Three: **Uses vocal variety in rate, pitch, & intensity.**

_____ _____ _____

Competency Four: **Avoids long (unintended) pauses in Speech Presentation.**

_____ _____ _____

Competency Five: **Uses physical behaviors (gestures) that support the verbal message.**

_____ _____ _____

Time: _____

Comments/Suggestions for speaker improvement:
(Also see Sprague text p. 168 – "Speaking Impromptu")

_____

_____

_____

_____

_____

_____

Public Speaking Competency Feedback and Development Form

**Highlighted items need more development

	Current level			
Organization and Content:	-	*OK*	+	++
Introduction · preview · attention getter · credibility · reason for listening				
Transitions · obvious · pause				
Organizational Pattern · clear · appropriate				
Central Idea · identifiable · focused				
Supporting Materials · smooth · names · authoritative				
Conclusion · signal end · summarize · repeat main points · closure · integrated				
Logistics · appropriate topic selection · appropriate length of speech · use of notes				
Delivery:				
Language · concrete · vivid · stories · avoid jargon				
Voice Quality · volume · rate · tone · flow				
Vocal Variety · inflection · pauses				
Kinesics · professional · energy · confident				
Eye Contact · scan · gaze · linger · inclusive				
Gestures · purposeful · integrated				
Utilization of Space · step up · step out				
Visual Aid(s):				
Design · clear · visible · professional				
Integration · smooth · purposeful				

Impromptu Speech

(From the Competent Speaker Form adopted from the National Communication Association)

Name_____   Date_____

PRESENTATIONAL COMPETENCIES

Competency Levels
Low / Moderate / High

Competency One: **Uses an effective attention-getter.**

_____ _____ _____

Competency Two: **Uses language appropriately**.

_____ _____ _____

Competency Three: **Uses vocal variety in rate, pitch, & intensity.**

_____ _____ _____

Competency Four: **Avoids long (unintended) pauses in Speech Presentation.**

_____ _____ _____

Competency Five: **Uses physical behaviors (gestures) that support the verbal message.**

_____ _____ _____

Time: _____

Comments/Suggestions for speaker improvement:
(Also see Sprague text p. 168 – "Speaking Impromptu")

_____

_____

_____

_____

_____

_____

Name ____________________

Public Speaking Competency Feedback and Development Form

**Highlighted items need more development — Current level

Organization and Content:	-	*OK*	+	++
Introduction · preview · attention getter · credibility · reason for listening				
Transitions · obvious · pause				
Organizational Pattern · clear · appropriate				
Central Idea · identifiable · focused				
Supporting Materials · smooth · names · authoritative				
Conclusion · signal end · summarize · repeat main points · closure · integrated				
Logistics · appropriate topic selection · appropriate length of speech · use of notes				
Delivery:				
Language · concrete · vivid · stories · avoid jargon				
Voice Quality · volume · rate · tone · flow				
Vocal Variety · inflection · pauses				
Kinesics · professional · energy · confident				
Eye Contact · scan · gaze · linger · inclusive				
Gestures · purposeful · integrated				
Utilization of Space · step up · step out				
Visual Aid(s):				
Design · clear · visible · professional				
Integration · smooth · purposeful				

Impromptu Speech

(From the Competent Speaker Form adopted from the National Communication Association)

Name_____   Date_____

PRESENTATIONAL COMPETENCIES

<u>Competency Levels</u>
Low / Moderate / High

Competency One: **Uses an effective attention-getter.**

_____ _____ _____

Competency Two: **Uses language appropriately.**

_____ _____ _____

Competency Three: **Uses vocal variety in rate, pitch, & intensity.**

_____ _____ _____

Competency Four: **Avoids long (unintended) pauses in Speech Presentation.**

_____ _____ _____

Competency Five: **Uses physical behaviors (gestures) that support the verbal message.**

_____ _____ _____

Time: _____

Comments/Suggestions for speaker improvement:
(Also see Sprague text p. 168 – "Speaking Impromptu")

_____

_____

_____

_____

_____

_____

Name ____________________

Public Speaking Competency Feedback and Development Form

**Highlighted items need more development — Current level

Organization and Content:	-	*OK*	+	++
Introduction · preview · attention getter · credibility · reason for listening				
Transitions · obvious · pause				
Organizational Pattern · clear · appropriate				
Central Idea · identifiable · focused				
Supporting Materials · smooth · names · authoritative				
Conclusion · signal end · summarize · repeat main points · closure · integrated				
Logistics · appropriate topic selection · appropriate length of speech · use of notes				
Delivery:				
Language · concrete · vivid · stories · avoid jargon				
Voice Quality · volume · rate · tone · flow				
Vocal Variety · inflection · pauses				
Kinesics · professional · energy · confident				
Eye Contact · scan · gaze · linger · inclusive				
Gestures · purposeful · integrated				
Utilization of Space · step up · step out				
Visual Aid(s):				
Design · clear · visible · professional				
Integration · smooth · purposeful				

Impromptu Speech

(From the Competent Speaker Form adopted from the National Communication Association)

Name_____   Date_____

PRESENTATIONAL COMPETENCIES

Competency Levels
Low / Moderate / High

Competency One: **Uses an effective attention-getter.**

_____ _____ _____

Competency Two: **Uses language appropriately**.

_____ _____ _____

Competency Three: **Uses vocal variety in rate, pitch, & intensity.**

_____ _____ _____

Competency Four: **Avoids long (unintended) pauses in Speech Presentation.**

_____ _____ _____

Competency Five: **Uses physical behaviors (gestures) that support the verbal message.**

_____ _____ _____

Time: _____

Comments/Suggestions for speaker improvement:
(Also see Sprague text p. 168 – "Speaking Impromptu")

_____

_____

_____

_____

_____

_____

Name _____

Public Speaking Competency Feedback and Development Form

**Highlighted items need more development

	Current level			
Organization and Content:	-	*OK*	+	++
Introduction · preview · attention getter · credibility · reason for listening				
Transitions · obvious · pause				
Organizational Pattern · clear · appropriate				
Central Idea · identifiable · focused				
Supporting Materials · smooth · names · authoritative				
Conclusion · signal end · summarize · repeat main points · closure · integrated				
Logistics · appropriate topic selection · appropriate length of speech · use of notes				
Delivery:				
Language · concrete · vivid · stories · avoid jargon				
Voice Quality · volume · rate · tone · flow				
Vocal Variety · inflection · pauses				
Kinesics · professional · energy · confident				
Eye Contact · scan · gaze · linger · inclusive				
Gestures · purposeful · integrated				
Utilization of Space · step up · step out				
Visual Aid(s):				
Design · clear · visible · professional				
Integration · smooth · purposeful				

Impromptu Speech

(From the Competent Speaker Form adopted from the National Communication Association)

Name_____   Date_____

PRESENTATIONAL COMPETENCIES

<u>Competency Levels</u>
Low / Moderate / High

Competency One: **Uses an effective attention-getter.**

_____ _____ _____

Competency Two: **Uses language appropriately**.

_____ _____ _____

Competency Three: **Uses vocal variety in rate, pitch, & intensity.**

_____ _____ _____

Competency Four: **Avoids long (unintended) pauses in Speech Presentation.**

_____ _____ _____

Competency Five: **Uses physical behaviors (gestures) that support the verbal message.**

_____ _____ _____

Time: _____

Comments/Suggestions for speaker improvement:
(Also see Sprague text p. 168 – "Speaking Impromptu")

_____
_____
_____
_____
_____
_____

Public Speaking Competency Feedback and Development Form

**Highlighted items need more development

Current level

Organization and Content:	-	*OK*	+	++
Introduction · preview · attention getter · credibility · reason for listening				
Transitions · obvious · pause				
Organizational Pattern · clear · appropriate				
Central Idea · identifiable · focused				
Supporting Materials · smooth · names · authoritative				
Conclusion · signal end · summarize · repeat main points · closure · integrated				
Logistics · appropriate topic selection · appropriate length of speech · use of notes				
Delivery:				
Language · concrete · vivid · stories · avoid jargon				
Voice Quality · volume · rate · tone · flow				
Vocal Variety · inflection · pauses				
Kinesics · professional · energy · confident				
Eye Contact · scan · gaze · linger · inclusive				
Gestures · purposeful · integrated				
Utilization of Space · step up · step out				
Visual Aid(s):				
Design · clear · visible · professional				
Integration · smooth · purposeful				

Speech Evaluation Form Definitions

Organization:	
Introduction	Can make or break your speech?
Attention	The first words out of your mouth need to capture our attention. Dive straight into your speech. Do not start with extraneous phrases such as "Hi, my name is…" and "Let me start with…"
Reason	Sell us on the importance of listening. Be obvious.
Credibility	Why should we listen to you? Don't assume we already consider you credible on the subject. Toot your own horn.
Preview	Tell us when you are going to tell us. We need to know how many main points there will be and what they are called.
Transitions	How you get from the intro to your first main point, and between each main point. Many audience members forget the one after the preview statement. You need to use internal previews and internal summaries.
Obvious	Call attention to the fact that you are changing points, we are likely to miss the transition otherwise.
Pause	Take a breath. Don't rush.
Organizational Pattern	Can be chronological, spatial, cause-effect, problem-solution, or topical. The action speech requires that you use the modified version of Monroe's Motivated Sequence.
Clear	We need to know what you are going to cover and in what order. The order of your main points in your preview statement should be the same as in your speech.
Appropriate	It needs to be so intuitive that we can follow along without thought. If we have to think about how A links to B links to C, you've lost us. As a general rule, don't have more than three points or more than three sub-points within a main point.
Central Idea	The "take home" message of your speech.
Identifiable	It should be crystal clear what you want and why. Your central idea needs to be obvious.
Focused	Your desired outcome needs to be surgically precise. What exactly is it you want us to think, feel, or do? Don't expect us to connect the dots.
Supporting Materials	You must orally cite your sources.
Smooth	Give just enough information about your source for us to recognize its value without interrupting the natural flow of your speech.

Names	Drop names; typically the author's last name (or the name of the organization) and year.
Authoritative	Cite credible sources. Opinions are considered weak while research is strong. The fact that your brother says Starbucks has the best coffee counts as an oral citation, but would lack authoritativeness unless you also told us that he is a recognized leader in coffee tasting research.
Conclusion	The conclusion is just an echo of your speech. Don't add new information here.
Signal End	Make it clear you are starting your conclusion.
Repeat Main Points	Tell us what you told us. Keep the order consistent; think broken record.
Closure	You began your speech with an attention getter, tie back to that so we have something to remember.
Topic Selection	
Appropriate	This means appropriate for the audience and this type of speech.

Delivery:	
Vocal Delivery	
Language	Word choice. Avoid using foul language for shock value only.
Concrete	Descriptors that appeal to our senses of sight, touch, taste, smell and hearing.
Vivid	Lots of detail that appeal to our senses. Don't confuse vividness with KISS. You are only allowed 2-3 main points with 2-3 sub-points each, so don't give us the 32 reasons to live at the Regency. But you need to give us vivid descriptions of the 2-3 that you keep. Fill the 70% of the 30/70 Rule with rich, descriptive examples.
Stories	Spin your information into story form. Facts sprinkled into a story are remembered much better than a simple list of facts.
Jargon	Don't use industry specific language. Use simple, everyday language.
Voice Quality	Your natural voice
Volume	Is it loud enough for everyone to hear?
Rate	Is it unnaturally fast or slow?
Tone	Does it sound like you are bored? You have to project more energy than you expect from us.
Flow	Do you keep your lips moving or do you draw attention to momentary lapses of consciousness?

Vocal Variety	Speak in an engaged, conversational manner
Inflection	Avoid being monotone. Speak like you actually care about your topic.
Pauses	Stop and breathe. Our brains need time to process what you are saying. Without breaks in the flow of information, we shut down and let everything you say flow out the other ear.
Non-verbal Delivery	
Kinesics	Body language
Professional	Behave in a manner consistent with your age and the college setting.
Energy	Show some enthusiasm. This is harder than one would think because our tendency is to shrink into our shells when nervous. You have to be open to allowing others to see your passion for the subject. Without it, you're wasting everyone's time.
Confident	Stand up straight, make eye contact, project, and smile.
Eye Contact	Absolutely essential, and unfortunately there is no way to fake it. Frequently, this is where people lose a lot of points on the first speech.
Scan	Keep your eyes moving around the room.
Gaze	At least 85% of your time should be spent looking directly at the audience, not your notes or the screen, floor or ceiling.
Linger	Focus on individuals long enough for them to know that you are speaking directly to them, but not so long that it feels creepy.
Inclusive	Include everyone, not just me (or the person on the opposite side as me) and not just your friends in class.
Gestures	Hand and body movements and posture.
Purposeful	Is there a reason for your gestures? Twirling your hair or clicking a pen distract from your presentation and interfere with the transparency of your message. But these are the type of unintentional nonverbals that can be corrected with focused attention and move you from being a good public speaker to being a great public speaker. Don't pace back and forth with little attention paid to purposeful or motivated movement. Your movements should appear like they have meaning, versus just random pacing.
Integrated	Do they flow with the speech? Fancy dance moves are pointless if they don't match the rhythm of the song.
Utilization of Space	Get out from behind the podium.
Step Out	Break the side plane of the podium.

Step Up	Take one step closer to the audience.

Visual Aid(s):	
Design	Video or audio clips that exceed 30 seconds are not appropriate for most of our speech presentations.
Clear	The connection between what you are showing us and the point being made needs to be made so obvious that we don't have to stop and think about it.
Visible	Make sure that the font is not too small. And avoid loading up on too much text.
Professional	Appears like you put a lot of thought into preparing your visual aid. People often use visual aids in amateurish ways that look tacky. Don't be tacky.
Integration	Look like you are in control of your visuals, not the other way around.
Preparation	Make sure everything is turned on and you know how the equipment works BEFORE you start speaking. The most common error is failing to check the volume when you have video clips with audio.
Concealed	The most common example of bad technique is having all your sub-points appear at once. You want to use the *Animation* feature in programs like PowerPoint to keep each sub-point hidden until you are ready to talk about each.
Smooth	Having to switch between various screens or programs looks amateurish. With advance planning and a little preparation, there is no reason you should have to fiddle with YouTube screens.
Purposeful	Does the visual fit appropriately within the purpose of the speech or is it simply tacked on?

Notes:	
Use of Notes	Using notes is perfectly acceptable. I'm looking for effective, but unobtrusive, use of notes. You should be able to see what you need with a quick flick of your eyes, without drawing attention to what you're doing.